Updated to include instruction for all NEW CPIs and NJ ASK Practice

Measuring Up®

to the

New Jersey Core Curriculum Content Standards

and Success Strategies for the NJ ASK

Language Arts Literacy

This book is customized for New Jersey and the lessons match the New Jersey Core Curriculum Content Standards. The Measuring Up® program includes instructional worktexts and Preliminary Assessment of Skills and Knowledge (PASK), preliminary diagnostic tests, which are available separately.

Grade 3

800-822-1080
www.NJStandardsHelp.com

PEOPLES PUBLISHING GROUP
299 Market Street, Saddle Brook, NJ 07663

Pg. 40, "Crystal Creations" Reproduced with permission. Copyright © Exploratorium, www.exploratorium.edu; pg. 58, "The Moon Landing Hoax" from Nasa Kids website, March 30, 2001; pg. 59, photograph courtesy of NASA; pg. 65, "When Whales Exhale" from *When Whales Exhale and Other Poems* by Constance Levy, Margaret K. McElderry Books, Simon & Schuster Children's Publishing Division; pg. 68, "The Toaster" from LAUGHING TIME: COLLECTED NONSENSE by William Jay Smith. Reprinted by permission of Farrar, Straus and Giroux, LLC; pg. 78, "Since Hannah Moved Away" by Judith Viorst, from *The Random House Book of Poetry for Children*, Copyright © 1983; pg. 82, "Bottle Penguin" by Debbie Anilonis, Copyright © Highlights for Children, Inc., Columbus Ohio; pg. 142, "The Swing" by Robert Louis Stevenson; pg. 175, "Oops!" Copyright © by Bruce Lansky. Reprinted from *Miles and Smiles* with permission from Meadowbrook Press; pg. 197, "Too Busy" Copyright © by Bruce Lansky. Reprinted from *Miles of Smiles* with permission from Meadowbrook Press; pg. 222, "A Captain's Cat" by Laurie Byro, published by Cricket Magazine, October 1999, Copyright © 1999 by Laurie Byro. Reprinted by permission of the author; pg. 249, "A Snake Named Rover" Copyright © by Maxine Jeffris. Reprinted from *Kids Pick the Funniest Poems* with permission of Meadowbrook Press; pg. 258, "Lucky Trade" Copyright © by Matthew Fredericks. Reprinted from *If Kids Ruled the School* with permission of Meadowbrook Press; pg. 264, "From the Elephant Pit" From the award winning web site: Absolutely Whootie: Stories to Grow By http://www.storiestogrowby.com), where ethical and entertaining fairytales and folk tales are presented for story lovers worldwide. Copyright © Elaine L. Lindy. This story is published by and reprinted with permission of Whootie Owl International, LLC; pg. 271, "The Duel" By Eugene Field; Writer's Checklist, Assessment Guide for Open-Ended Items and Speaker's Checklist, permission granted by the New Jersey Department of Education

New Jersey Advisory Panel

Georgeanne Herbeck, District Language Arts Supervisor, K–12, Perth Amboy Public Schools

Alberta Alleva, 3rd Grade Teacher, Stephen J. Gerace School, Pequannock Township

Rosanne Manganelli, Reading Specialist, Pequannock Township Public Schools

Publisher: Diane Miller
Editorial Development: BBE Associates, Ltd.
Editorial Director: Marie Spano
Editor: Scott Caffrey
Director of Marketing: Victoria Ameer Kiely
Pre-Press & Production Manager: Doreen Smith
Designer: Charles Donahue
Project Manager: Jennifer Heart

Desktop Publishing Assistants: Sylvia Vidal, Steven Genzano, Reiko Radomski, Carolyn Eldenstein, Alexis Rodriguez
Copy Editor: Dee Josephson
Photo Researcher/Permissions Manager: Kristine Liebman
Illustrators: Armando Báez, Sal Esposito, Steven Cavallo, Laurie Harden, Rieko Radomski, Ed Tadiello
Cover Design: Yadiro Henriquez, Cynthia Mackowicz, Michele Sakow

ISBN 1-58984-941-8

Measuring Up® Contents

Standard	CPIs	Lesson	
3.1	A1, A2, D3, E1, E4, G1, G2, G6, G7, G8, G9, G10, G11, G12, H2	**1**	Prereading: Learning Skills for Reading Narrative Selections 2
3.2	A2, C3, D7		
3.3	C1, C2		
3.4	B2, B3		
3.5	A1, A2, B1, B2		
3.1	A1, A3, B1, C1, C2, D1, D2, D3, E1, E2, E3, E4, G1, G2, G3, G4, G7, G8, G12, G14, H2	**2**	Guided Reading Instruction: Practicing Skills for Reading Narrative Selections 9
3.2	A1, D1, D3		
3.3	A1, A4, C1, C3		
3.5	A2, B1		

CHAPTER 1 Guided Reading for a Narrative Selection (continued)

CHAPTER 2 Guided Reading for Everyday and Persuasive Selections 21

CHAPTER 3 Guided Reading for an Informational Selection .46

CHAPTER 3 Guided Reading for an Informational Selection (continued)

Standard	CPIs	Lesson
3.1	B1, C1, C2, C3, D2, E1, E2, E3, E4, F1, F3, F4, G1, G2, G3, G4, G6, G7, G8, G10, G13, G14, H3	
3.2	A1, A3, D7	

Standard	CPIs	Lesson
3.1	A1, A2, D1, D3, E1, E4, G1, G2, G6, G7, G8, G9, G10, G11, G12, G13, H2	
3.2	A2, C3, D7	
3.3	B2, B3	
3.4	A1, B2, B3	
3.5	A1, A2, B1, B2	
3.1	A1, A3, B1, C1, C2, C3, D1, D2, D3, E1, E2, E3, E4, F1, F2, F3, F4, F5, G1, G2, G5, G6, G7, G8, G9, G10, G11, G12, G13, H3	
3.3	A1, A4, B2	
3.4	A1, A2, B3	
3.5	A2, B1	
3.1	B1, C1, C2, C3, D2, E1, E2, E3, E4, F1, F3, F4, F5, G1, G2, G5, G6, G7, G8, G9, G10, G13, H3	
3.2	A1, A3, D7	

Standard	CPIs
3.1	A1, A2, B1, C1, C2, C3, D2, E1, E2, E3, E4, F1, F2, F3, F5, G1, G2, G3, G4, G5, G6, G7, G8, G9, G10, G13, G14, H2, H3
3.2	A1, A3, D7

Correlation Guide to the New Jersey Core Curriculum Content Standards

See page 274 for the complete Measuring Up® Correlation to the New Jersey Core Curriculum Content Standards.

> The New Jersey Core Curriculum Content Standards are organized into five language arts literacy standards, each of which has lettered strands and numbered Cumulative Progress Indicators (CPIs).

Students and teachers can assess mastery of each standard in every unit, chapter, and lesson. A check mark in the appropriate box indicates mastery; an X indicates a skill that needs further review.

Describes each language arts literacy standard

Gives the details of the strands and Cumulative Progress Indicators (CPIs) in each standard and indicates the lessons in which they are either covered, to be covered, or have been previously covered

Correlation to the New Jersey Core Curriculum Content Standards

This worktext is customized to the Core Curriculum Content Standards and Cumulative Progress Indicators and will help you prepare for the New Jersey Grade Three Assessment of Skills and Knowledge (NJ ASK).

As the lesson for each Cumulative Progress Indicator (CPI) is completed, place a ✓ to indicate Mastery or an X to indicate Review Needed.

Unit 1: Reading and Viewing Chapter 1: Guided Reading for a Narrative Selection	1	2	3	NA	NA	NA	NA	NA	NA	Un. Rev	End Rev
Standard 3.1 (Reading) All students will understand and apply the knowledge of sounds, letters, and words in written English to become independent and fluent readers, and will read a variety of materials and texts with fluency and comprehension.											
A1. CONCEPTS ABOUT PRINT/TEXT Recognize that printed materials provide specific information.	★	★	✓							★	★
A2. CONCEPTS ABOUT PRINT/TEXT Recognize purposes for print conventions such as end-sentence punctuation, paragraphing, and bold print.	★	✓	✓							★	★
A3. CONCEPTS ABOUT PRINT/TEXT Use a glossary or index to locate information in a text.	○	★	✓							✓	✓
B1. PHONOLOGICAL AWARENESS (INCLUDES PHONEMIC AWARENESS) Demonstrate a sophisticated sense of sound-symbol relationships, including all phonemes (e.g., blends, digraphs, dipthongs)	○	★	★							★	★
C1. DECODING AND WORD RECOGNITION Know sounds for a range of prefixes and suffixes (e.g., re-, ex-, -ment, -tion).	○	★	★							★	★
C2. DECODING AND WORD RECOGNITION Use letter-sound knowledge and structural analysis to decode words.	○	★	★							★	★
C3. DECODING AND WORD RECOGNITION Use context to accurately read words with more than one pronunciation.	○	○	★							★	★
D1. FLUENCY Recognize grade-level words accurately and with ease so that a text sounds like spoken language when read aloud.	○	★	✓							✓	✓
D2. FLUENCY Read longer text and chapter books independently and silently.	○	★	★							★	★
D3. FLUENCY Read aloud with proper phrasing, inflection, and intonation.	★	★	✓							✓	✓
E1. READING STRATEGIES (BEFORE, DURING, AFTER READING) Set purpose for reading and check to verify or change predictions during/after reading.	★	★	★							★	★
E2. READING STRATEGIES (BEFORE, DURING, AFTER READING) Monitor comprehension and accuracy while reading in context and self-correct errors.	○	★	★							★	★
E3. READING STRATEGIES (BEFORE, DURING, AFTER READING) Use pictures and context clues to assist with decoding of new words.	○	★	★							★	★
E4. READING STRATEGIES (BEFORE, DURING, AFTER READING) Develop and use graphic organizers to build on experiences and extend learning.	★	★	★							★	★
F1. VOCABULARY AND CONCEPT DEVELOPMENT Spell previously studied words and spelling patterns accurately.	○	○	★							★	★
F3. VOCABULARY AND CONCEPT DEVELOPMENT Infer word meanings from taught roots, prefixes, and suffixes.	○	○	★							★	★
F4. VOCABULARY AND CONCEPT DEVELOPMENT Use a grade-appropriate dictionary with assistance from teacher.	○	○	★							✓	✓
G1. COMPREHENSION SKILLS AND RESPONSE TO TEXT Recognize purpose of the text.	★	★	★							★	★
G2. COMPREHENSION SKILLS AND RESPONSE TO TEXT Distinguish cause/effect, fact/opinion, main idea/supporting details in interpreting texts.	★	★	★							★	★

Column headers above: Review Skill, Mastered Skill, Lessons

★ Standards covered   ○ Standards to be covered   ✓ Standards previously covered

Describes the symbols used to indicate the lessons in which a standard is either covered, to be covered, or has been previously covered

Measuring Up
to the
**New Jersey Core Curriculum
Content Standards**
and Success Strategies for the NJ ASK

Dear Student,

How do you get better at the things you do? You practice! Just like with sports or other activities, the key to success in school is practice, practice, practice.

This book will help you review and practice reading, writing, speaking, listening, and viewing strategies and skills. These are the strategies and skills you need to know to measure up on the *New Jersey Assessment of Skills and Knowledge*, or *NJ ASK*, for your grade. Practicing these methods now will help you do better in your work all year.

There are three units in this book. Unit 1 gives you practice in reading and viewing. Unit 2 gives you practice in writing. Finally, Unit 3 gives you practice in speaking and listening.

Each lesson of Unit 1 consists of three main sections:

- **Focus on the New Jersey CCCS** introduces the reading and viewing skills covered in the lesson.
- **Guided Reading Instruction** shows you the skills you will need for successful learning.
- **NJ ASK Practice** gives you practice in answering test-type questions.

Each lesson of Units 2 and 3 consists of four main sections:

- **Focus on the New Jersey CCCS** introduces the writing, speaking, or listening skills covered in the lesson.
- **Guided Instruction** shows you the skills you will need for successful learning.
- **Apply the New Jersey CPIs** helps you understand important ideas and skills by using what you have learned.
- **NJ ASK Practice** gives you practice in answering test-type questions.

There are many chances for you to practice for the test. At the end of Units 1 and 2 are Unit Reviews. At the end of the book is a big End-of-Book Review. Each review has a story, poem, and/or writing prompt to test your understanding. You will answer multiple-choice and open-ended questions and write compositions just like you will on the test. Many of these questions and prompts are more difficult and will help you prepare for taking tests.

In the spring, you will take the *New Jersey Assessment of Skills and Knowledge (NJ ASK)* exam. It will be an important step forward. The *NJ ASK* will show how well you measure up to the CPIs. It is just one of the many important tests you will take.

Have a great year!

PEOPLES
PUBLISHING GROUP

Measuring Up
to the
**New Jersey Core Curriculum
Content Standards**
and Success Strategies for the NJ ASK

To Parents and Families,

All students need reading, writing, speaking, listening, and viewing skills to succeed in school and in life. New Jersey educators have created grade-appropriate standards called the New Jersey Core Curriculum Content Standards (CCCS) and Cumulative Progress Indicators (CPIs), for these skills. The CPIs describe what New Jersey students should know at different grade levels. Students need to meet these standards, as measured by the *New Jersey Assessment of Skills and Knowledge*, or *NJ ASK*, given in the spring.

The *NJ ASK* is directly related to the revised New Jersey Core Curriculum Content Standards (CCCS) and the CPIs. The CPIs emphasize higher-level thinking skills. Students must learn to consider, analyze, interpret, and evaluate instead of just recalling simple facts.

Measuring Up® will help your child review the CCCS and CPIs and prepare for all language arts literacy exams. It contains:

- lessons that focus on practicing the CCCS and CPIs;

- varied reading, writing, speaking, listening, and viewing selections and activities;

- **Guided Instruction** in which questions are provided that guide learning by highlighting particular skills;

- **Apply the New Jersey CPIs,** which shows how individual CPIs can be understood by answering questions and performing activities;

- **NJ ASK Practice,** which shows how individual CPIs can be understood through multiple-choice questions, open-ended questions, and writing prompts;

- **Unit Reviews,** which give practice with more difficult multiple-choice questions, open-ended questions, and writing prompts that require higher-level thinking.

Get involved with your child's learning process! Your involvement is crucial to your child's success. Here are some suggestions:

Reading

Bring books and magazines into the home. Show that you enjoy reading and you believe it is important. Browse the shelves of bookstores and the library together. If you have a computer and access to the World Wide Web, surf together to look for information about topics you both find interesting. If you don't have access, visit your local library and learn the process together.

Writing

Take pride in your child's writing. Post it on the refrigerator. Keep a scrapbook. Write cards to family and friends together. Help them write thank-you notes. Suggest that they keep a personal diary and write in it every day.

Speaking, Listening, and Viewing

As you listen to the radio and watch television or movies, engage your child in a discussion about what you hear and see. Question the information being presented. Talk about how the information relates to your own experience. Ask for your child's reactions.

Work with us this year to ensure your child's success. Reading, writing, speaking, listening, and viewing are essential not only for school but in the real world as well. They will give pleasure throughout your child's life.

PEOPLES
PUBLISHING GROUP

What's Ahead in Measuring Up

What's Ahead in Measuring Up® **to the** *New Jersey Core Curriculum Content Standards*

This book was created for New Jersey students. Each lesson, question, and selection is aimed at helping you master the New Jersey Core Content Curriculum Standards (CCCS) and the Cumulative Progress Indicators (CPIs) for your grade. They will also help you with other exams you may take during this school year.

About the *NJ ASK* **Test**

New Jersey educators have developed the New Jersey Core Content Curriculum Standards and CPIs for language arts literacy. These standards spell out exactly what students at different grade levels should know. The *NJ ASK* measures how well students have mastered the New Jersey standards and CPIs. Questions are written to go along with and meet the following New Jersey language arts literacy Standards:

New Jersey Core Curriculum Content Standards

Standard 3.1 (Reading)

All students will understand and apply the knowledge of sounds, letters, and words in written English to become independent and fluent readers, and will read a variety of materials and texts with fluency and comprehension.

Standard 3.2 (Writing)
All students will write in clear, concise, organized language that varies in content and form for different audiences and purposes.

Standard 3.3 (Speaking)
All students will speak in clear, concise, organized language that varies in content and form for different audiences and purposes.

Standard 3.4 (Listening)
All students will listen actively to information from a variety of sources in a variety of situations.

Standard 3.5 (Viewing and Media Literacy)
All students will access, view, evaluate, and respond to print, nonprint, and electronic texts and resources.

Measuring Up® on Multiple-Choice Questions

A multiple-choice question has two parts. The first part is the **stem**, or question. It has a number in front of it. The second part is the **choices**, or answers. They have letters in front of them. The letters are in circles that you will fill in to choose the correct answer.

There are some strategies for answering multiple-choice questions. Try these:
- Skim all the questions first. Start by answering the ones you think are the easiest.
- Cross out the answer choices you know are definitely wrong. Then choose from the answers that are left.
- If a question refers to a paragraph, make sure you reread that paragraph.
- Some questions will be more difficult than others. The exact answers are not right there in the paragraph or selection. You must connect the ideas and information to come up with the right answers.
- Even if you don't know the answer, you can make a good guess based on what you know and get the question right.
- Be sure of your answers. Check and double-check your answers before you turn in the test.

Measuring Up® on Open-Ended Questions

Open-ended questions require you to draw conclusions about selections and explain your reasoning. These questions appear with reading selections on the *New Jersey ASK for Language Arts Literacy*. Here are some tips for answering open-ended questions:
- Read carefully. Because you do not have answer choices as a way to check yourself, it is important to use your time wisely and follow all the steps carefully.
- Once you have an answer, carefully write it down.
- Use information from the selection to help you write an explanation of your reasoning.
- Read over your answer. Is it clear and easy to follow? Do you need to make your ideas more clear? If you are having difficulty reading it, the scorer certainly will, too.

Measuring Up® on Writing Prompts

The test has two different kinds of writing prompts. The first kind has a full-page picture. You will be asked to write a story based on what you see in the picture. The second kind is a written prompt. The prompt is connected to a poem that you will read. You are expected to write a composition based on the poem and the prompt. Here are some tips for writing to prompts:
- Organize your thoughts, ideas, and details first.
- Carefully write your composition. Be sure your ideas are well thought-out, that you use the proper punctuation, and that your spelling is the best it can be.
- Read over your composition once or twice and make any changes you feel are necessary. If it makes sense to you, chances are it will make sense to the reader.

Strategies to Measure Up

There are some general test-preparation strategies you can use to succeed. Here are a few useful tips:

- Start getting ready now. Spend a few minutes a day practicing answers to test questions.
- Get a good night's sleep the night before the test.
- Eat a good breakfast.
- Keep telling yourself that you will do well. Then you probably will. That's what it means to "think positively."
- Wear a watch. Keep track of time so that you finish the whole test.

Higher-Level Thinking Skills

Higher-level thinking skills are important on the *NJ ASK*. When you use higher-level thinking skills, you do more than just recall information. On the *NJ ASK*, some questions ask you to make judgments, inferences, predictions, draw conclusions, take a position and support it, and so on. For instance, instead of asking you what a character wore, a question might ask you how the character's clothes affected the way she acted. Or, instead of asking you how something happened, a question might ask you why something happened.

Measuring Up® on Unit Reviews

A special feature of Measuring Up® are the Unit Reviews. They were created to give you practice and build your confidence for taking difficult tests. The more you practice answering hard questions the more prepared you will be to succeed. At the end of the book is a big End-of-Book Review.

You will learn a lot in Measuring Up®. You will review and practice the New Jersey CPIs. You will practice for the *NJ ASK*. Finally, you will build your stamina to answer tough questions. You will more than measure up. You'll be a smashing success.

Focus on the New Jersey CCCS

What is your favorite story? Who are the people in the story? Why do you like this story more than others? How can knowing how to read different kinds of literature help you succeed on the *New Jersey ASK Language Arts Literacy* test?

Guided Instruction

Directions Look at the pictures below. Then read the numbered sentences. Follow the instructions for each sentence.

1. Look at the animals in the picture. One is doing something that cannot be real. Color it green.

2. One animal could be real. Color it orange.

3. One is a person who could be in your class. Color this person's shirt blue.

4. Name a story you have read about a real animal. Name a story about an imaginary animal.

_____

_____

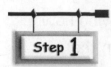

Step 1

Set a purpose for your reading.

WHAT IS NARRATIVE TEXT?

Directions Read the paragraphs. Look at the pictures. Answer the questions that follow.

Good stories can make a reader feel many different things. Reading a story can make us feel sad. We can see stories come to life in plays, movies, or on television. Stories can even be found in TV ads and on the Internet.

Some fiction stories are **realistic.** The events in the story might really have happened. In real life, you might know people like the characters. The people in *Little Women* by Louisa May Alcott were patterned after the writer's own family.

Other stories are fantastic. They are about strange and unusual characters and events. Babar the Elephant is a made-up character. No elephants talk like people do.

1. Which picture shows things that could be real? Draw a box around this picture.

2. Study what the picture shows. Is the picture about a person from the past or one who lives now?

3. What things in the picture helped you answer question 2?

    _____

    _____

    _____

4. One picture shows things that are fantastic. Draw a circle
    around this picture.

5. What kinds of things shown in the picture cannot be real?

    _____

    _____

    _____

6. How might these characters be like people you know?

    _____

    _____

    _____

7. Imagine what kinds of things might happen in this story.
    Write a sentence that tells about one thing that
    might happen.

    _____

    _____

    _____

Step 2

Recognize the organizational structure of the texts that you read.

WHAT ARE SOME DIFFERENT KINDS OF NARRATIVE TEXT?

You will read different kinds of selections for the *New Jersey ASK Language Arts Literacy* test. One will be a piece of **narrative text**. Then you will answer questions about it. The kinds of narrative text that you might see are short stories, myths, legends, or folktales.

Short Stories

A **short story** is a short work of literature. It might take you an hour or less to read a short story. Short stories may be realistic or fantastic. Short stories are often found in magazines. Have you ever read magazines like *Cricket, Boys' Quest,* or *Hopscotch for Girls*?

Myths, Legends, and Folktales

Myths, legends, and **folktales** are stories handed down from earlier times. Myths often tell about the gods and goddesses of a group of people. You have probably read and heard myths about Odin, Thor, and other gods and goddesses of Northern Europe. Legends and folktales often give colorful explanations for natural events. Many contain animal characters. You may have read an African tale about how the crocodile got its teeth.

Media Connection

You see and hear stories every day. TV shows and movies tell stories. They are **narratives**. Talk about some TV shows and movies you have seen. Which ones are realistic? Which ones are **fantastic?**

Directions Look at the pictures below. Answer the questions that follow.

1. Circle the picture that shows things that could be real.

2. What kinds of narrative might tell a story about this picture?

   _____

3. Draw a box around the thing that is fantastic.

4. What kinds of narrative might tell a story about this picture?

   _____

TEXT STRUCTURE

Authors put their stories together in certain ways. There are different parts that make up text structure. What are the parts of text structure?

Sequence of Events	**Sequence of events** is the order in which things happen. One thing happens to start the story. Then something else happens. A third event happens after that, and so on. As you read, think about what happens and when these things happen.
Plot	The events in a story follow a plan. This plan is called the **plot.** The plot tells what happens to the main character. This person, animal, or thing will usually have a problem. The plot tells how the character tries to solve the problem. The story ends when the problem is solved.
Setting	**Setting** is the time and place where a story happens.
End Punctuation	These are **periods**(.), **question marks**(?), and **exclamation points**(!). When you see each one, you know you have reached the end of a sentence. They also tell you how to read sentences aloud. Notice that your voice goes up at the end of a question.
Paragraphs	A **paragraph** is a group of sentences. All the sentences are about one idea or a point the writer is trying to make.
Point of View	One writer might tell things about other people. Sentences will include things like *he ran* or *she went*. A different writer may tell about something as if he or she took part in the story. These stories will have sentences that say things such as *I ran* or *I said*.
Bold Words	Important words are often shown as **bold**. These words help you find the main idea of a story.

Understand the
author's purpose
and the
reader's purpose.

HOW DO YOU MAKE INFERENCES AND CONCLUSIONS ABOUT NARRATIVE STORIES?

The people and things who talk and act in stories are called the **characters.** Authors use characters to help present the point, or **main idea,** of the story. You can understand the point by studying the actions, words, and thoughts of the characters. Stuart Little is a mouse that is the main character in the book *Stuart Little* by E. B. White. Laura Ingalls is the unforgettable girl in the *Little House* stories she wrote about herself. Think about how each of these characters thinks, talks, and acts. What ideas about life do the authors present with their characters?

A **reader's purpose** is to look at all the **details**, or happenings, of a story. Readers use these details to make a guess about the characters. This type of guess is called an **inference.** For example, you might read that most of the characters think another character is mean. However, from the details you read, you do not agree. You make an inference based on your reading that the person is really kind. As you put all of the details together, you see that your inference is right. In fact, the main point of the story is that the character is really different from what people thought. Putting all these details together helps you understand the main idea of the story.

Authors also try to get across a message about life in their stories. This type of message is called the **theme.** A story's theme may be a message that fits in your life, too. As you read each story, try to figure out its theme.

Here is a useful reading tool: As you read, list key events in the story. Also list details about the main characters. Use your list to write a **summary** of what you have read. Your summary will tell the most important ideas about the story in your words.

Step 4

Put your prereading skills together as you prepare to read.

Directions Answer the following questions.

1. You will read "Mrs. Tiggy-Winkle." It is about talking animals. Will it be a realistic story or a fantastic story?

_____

_____

2. Think about the plot of a story. What will the characters have to do in the short story that you will read?

_____

_____

_____

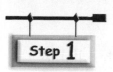

Step 1

Use skills to read and/or listen to whole texts.

You are about to read a story and answer questions about it. Write your answers on the Narrative Story Map on page 13. The questions will help you to:

- decide on the purpose of the story;
- name causes and effects, facts and opinions, and main ideas and supporting details;
- use pictures to understand the story's theme;
- use questions to examine the story;
- make decisions about the way the story is written;
- summarize the story;
- draw your own ideas about the plot, characters, setting, and theme, and read independently.

Step 2

Study important words from the story.

You will need to know the following words for the story. Read each one and think about its meaning. Look for the words as you read the story. Think about how each word is used in the story.

pinafore	a sleeveless dress fastened at the back and worn like an apron
handkerchief	a small piece of cloth used for blowing the nose

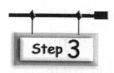

Step 3

Use word skills to increase your vocabulary.

WHAT ARE SOME TOOLS FOR LEARNING NEW WORDS?

You will see new words as you read stories, newspapers, magazines, directions, and all kinds of texts. You will also hear new words as you watch TV or movies, listen to the radio, or surf the Internet. How can you figure out what a new word means? One good place to start is by looking up the meaning of the word in a **dictionary** or **glossary.** There are also other strategies to use while you are reading.

Decide how to say the word

Break the new word into **syllables.** Pronounce each syllable. Then put the sounds together. Remember that two or more letters may stand for one sound. Say the letter *s* and then say the letter *n*. Then say them together—*sn*. Together, the letters have a slightly different sound than when you say them separately. Say the word *head*. What sound is formed by the letters *e* and *a* together? Sound out the word again. Knowing how the word sounds can help you remember its meaning.

Find the parts that make up a compound word

Sometimes breaking a word into parts can help you figure out its meaning. Two words might be combined to form one new word. *Sunrise* is the time when the sun comes up. *Sunrise* combines the meanings of both *sun* and *rise*. Think about how *handshake* and *playground* combine the meaning of two words into one.

Two or more words might state one idea. The **compound word** *ice cream cone* has a different meaning from just the words *ice, cream,* or *cone.* The words are joined to explain a whole idea. *Grade school* and *media center* are more examples of compound words.

Decide how the word fits in its context

Look at how the word is used in a sentence or paragraph. The words and ideas around a new word are called its **context.** Think about what the writer is saying in a sentence or paragraph. Examine pictures and captions used with the story. Decide what they tell you about the story and its message. Focus on the word you don't know. Sound it out. Think about the way it is used. Write down your own **definition.** Then look up the word in a glossary or dictionary. Check to see how well you defined the word.

Directions   Read each paragraph below. Say the underlined word aloud. Study the meaning of each sentence. Write a definition for the word. Use a dictionary or glossary to check your work.

1. Caleb didn't want to leave the park. He knew his mother was waiting. He slowly took off his skates. Then he <u>grudgingly</u> headed for home. Caleb took the long, slow way home.

   _____

   _____

   _____

2. The <u>hothouse</u> tomatoes were set at a low price. We bought three. They were cut into slices for our sandwiches. These tomatoes certainly didn't taste as good as the ones grown outside.

   _____

   _____

   _____

Step 4

Understand literary elements found in some stories.

Authors use different tools to tell their stories. Knowing about these tools will help you find a story's meaning.

Humor affects a reader's feelings. Writing that makes you laugh helps you feel like you are part of a story. Humor might be shown through a character who acts in an unusual way. This tool is also part of TV shows and movies. Scooby-Doo is a character who is always afraid. Most people have shared this feeling at times.

Another tool is **sarcasm.** Characters might make a statement that is said almost as a joke. Other characters and readers know that the statement is not true. For example, one character might walk into a wall while talking. Another character might say, "Nice job." You know the second character is pointing out that something went wrong. Look for sarcasm in TV shows, movies, speeches, plays, and skits.

Imagery helps readers form pictures. Suppose a writer says that a flower is "as yellow as the sun." You can just see that color in your mind. A writer might say that "an idea is a diamond." You know that the idea is a great one. Or, you might listen to someone give a speech about a vacation he had. Through his description, you can practically see the place he visited.

Directions Use the Narrative Story Map below as you read "Mrs. Tiggy-Winkle." Use it to take notes as you read. List important ideas about the story in the chart below.

Narrative Story Map

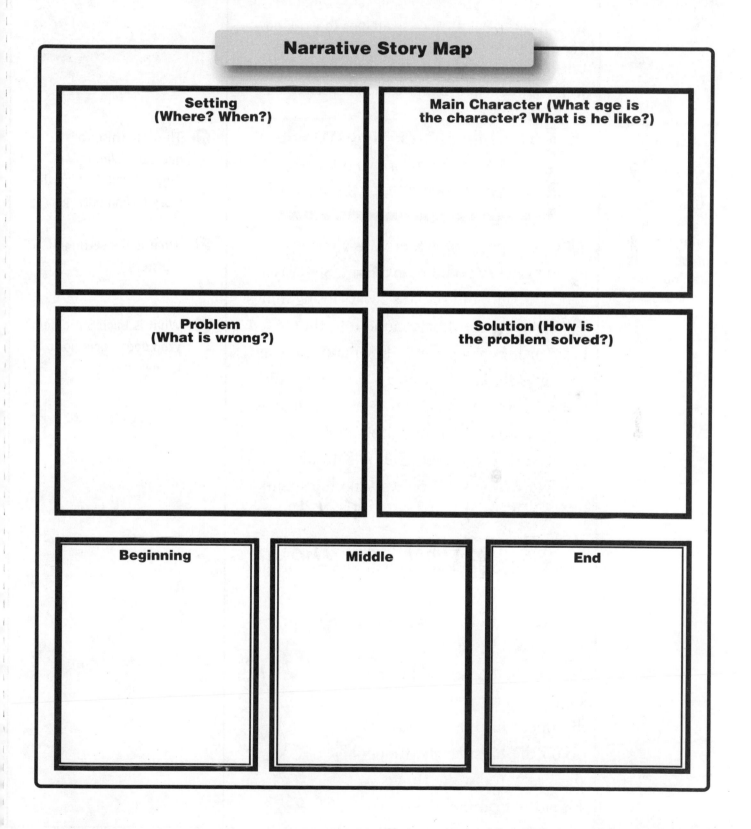

Setting
(Where? When?)

Main Character (What age is the character? What is he like?)

Problem
(What is wrong?)

Solution (How is the problem solved?)

Beginning

Middle

End

READING WITH COMPREHENSION

Guided Reading Instruction

| Reading Guide | Guided Questions |

Directions Put all your strategies to work now. They will help you read the story, "Mrs. Tiggy-Winkle." Look at the questions on the side. They will help you improve your comprehension.

Step 5

Understand stories by identifying point of view, facts from opinions, and story elements.

❶
The Tale of Mrs. Tiggy-Winkle
A Story by Beatrix Potter as retold by Cindy Bean

❷ Once upon a time there was a young girl named Lucie who lived on a farm. She was a good little girl, but she was always losing things! ❸ One fine day Lucie came into the farmyard. Her head was down and she was crying. "Oh darn," she said. "I've gone and lost another handkerchief. Now that makes three handkerchiefs and a pinafore lost! Have YOU seen them, Tabby Kitten?"

The Kitten went on washing her white paws, so Lucie turned to the hen, "Sally Henny-Penny, have you found my handkerchiefs?" But the hen just ran off into a barn, clucking all the way.

Poor little Lucie was so sad. She turned and looked up at the hill behind the barn. The hill was so high that it seemed to disappear into the clouds. Way up on the hillside, she thought she saw three white things spread out on the grass.

❶ The title raises a question. Who is Mrs. Tiggy-Winkle? Read the story to find out.

❷ What is the setting of the story? *Oh a farm*

❸ What is Lucie's problem? Who does Lucie go to for help? *She has lost another handkerchief.*

Reading Guide	Guided Questions

4 Lucie scrambled up the path as fast as her little legs could go. She ran up and up, faster and faster. Finally she stopped and turned to look behind her. She was up so high she could no longer see the farm anymore.

The path she was following came to an end under a big, heavy rock. The grass was short and green. Lucie noticed a small clothesline made of braided grass and sticks. There were clothespins everywhere, but no handkerchiefs.

5 "Oh, look here," Lucie said to herself. She saw a tiny wooden door in the side of the hill, near the rock. She thought she heard someone singing from inside. "How could this be?" she thought.

Curiously, Lucie bent down to knock on the door. "Who's there?" a sweet voice called out. "Come inside, if you please."

6 Lucie opened the door and crawled inside to find a nice, clean farm kitchen. But the ceiling was so low that Lucie's head almost bumped it. She took a look around. Everything in the kitchen was so small!

7 The kitchen was warm and smelled so good. At the table stood a very short, round person with a clothes iron in her hand. She had a little black nose that went sniffle, snuffle, sniffle and her little black eyes went twinkle, twinkle. Underneath her cap, Lucie noticed the little person had prickles instead of curls!

"Who are you?" Lucie asked. "Have you seen my handkerchiefs?"

The little person replied, "Oh yes, miss. My name is Mrs. Tiggy-Winkle." She took some things out of a basket and spread them on the table for Lucie to see.

4 Why does Lucie scramble, or run, up the hill? *she things she found her handky*

5 Do you think Lucie will go through a door that leads into a hill? Why? *Yes*

6 What is the setting of this part of the story? *in a kitchen, small*

7 What is Mrs. Tiggy-Winkle like? What kind of work do you think she does? *she is kind, is a mouse, rabit*

Reading Guide	Guided Questions
"There's one of my handkerchiefs!" Lucie said excitedly. "And there's my pinafore!" Mrs. Tiggy-Winkle ironed Lucie's pinafore. She took special care with it to impress Lucie. "Oh my, isn't that lovely!" said Lucie gratefully. Then Mrs. Tiggy-Winkle fetched something else out of the basket. "Why look, there's another handkerchief," said Lucie. "But it's red." "Oh no," replied Mrs. Tiggy-Winkle. "If you please, this one belongs to Mrs. Rabbit." She ironed the red handkerchief, then a pair of stockings for Sally Henny-Penny, and a pair of blue overalls belonging to Peter Rabbit. There were more of Lucie's handkerchiefs in the bottom of the basket, and Mrs. Tiggy-Winkle set about ironing them all. Then Mrs. Tiggy-Winkle made some nice hot tea-a cup for herself, and a cup for Lucie. They both sat down on the same bench in front of the fire to talk and drink some tea. Lucie noticed that Mrs. Tiggy-Winkle's hands were very brown and wrinkly and covered with soapsuds. Lucie also saw some prickles sticking out of her cap and gown, so she didn't want to sit too close. ❽ When they had finished their last drops of tea, they gathered together all the freshly ironed clothes-one tidy bundle for each customer. They folded up Lucie's handkerchiefs inside her clean pinafore, and they fastened it with a silver safety pin. Lucie and Mrs. Tiggy-Winkle trotted down the hill with all the bundles of clothes. Along the path, lots of little animals and birds came out from their homes to meet them and say hello. The very first animals that they met were	❽ What kind of worker is Mrs. Tiggy-Winkle?

Reading Guide	Guided Questions

Peter Rabbit and Benjamin Bunny.

9 Mrs. Tiggy-Winkle gave Peter Rabbit his blue overalls, and she gave Benjamin Bunny the little red handkerchief to give to old Mrs. Rabbit. Every single one of the little animals was so grateful to dear Mrs. Tiggy-Winkle for washing and ironing their clothes.

Lucie and Mrs. Tiggy-Winkle continued on their way down the hill. There was nothing left to carry but Lucie's one little bundle.

When they reached the bottom of the hill they stopped at the farmyard gate. Mrs. Tiggy-Winkle told Lucie to stop by someday soon for another cup of tea.

Lucie went through the gate with her bundle. She turned around to say thank you and good-bye to the tiny little washerwoman with the prickles under her cap.

But what a very strange thing! Mrs. Tiggy-Winkle didn't bother to wait for thanks or payment! She was running, running, running up the hill.

Where was her white ruffled cap? Where was her lovely shawl? And where were her print gown and pinafore?

And how very small Mrs. Tiggy-Winkle seemed, and how brown-and, why, she was covered all over with prickles!

Mrs. Tiggy-Winkle, as it turned out, was a roly-poly little hedgehog!

Some people say that Lucie must have been napping and dreaming by that farmyard gate. If that was the case, how could it be that she found her three white handkerchiefs and pinafore, all clean and bundled together with a silver safety pin?

10 And besides, other folks have seen that little wooden door in the side of the hill.

9 What are the animals' opinions of Mrs. Tiggy-Winkle?

10 a. Go back to the first question: Who is Mrs. Tiggy-Winkle?
b. Do you think Lucie really met a hedgehog who does washing and laundry? What parts of the story support your view?

Directions Use details from the story to answer the following questions.

1. Why is the title of this story "Mrs. Tiggy-Winkle"?

Ⓐ The story is about an unusual animal named Mrs. Tiggy-Winkle.

Ⓑ Lucie learns why her mother is called Mrs. Tiggy-Winkle.

Ⓒ Mrs. Tiggy-Winkle is the one who causes all the problems in the story.

Ⓓ All the animals go with Lucie to find Mrs. Tiggy-Winkle, the person in their favorite story.

2. What is the problem that must be solved?

Ⓐ Who is Mrs. Tiggy-Winkle?

Ⓑ Where are the animals' lost clothes?

Ⓒ Where are Lucie's lost handkerchiefs and pinafore?

Ⓓ Who lives at the top of the hill?

3. What kind of place is Mrs. Tiggy-Winkle's home?

Ⓐ a friendly place where all the animals gather

Ⓑ a secret tiny place like the homes of people

Ⓒ a place that scares Mrs. Tiggy-Winkle at times

Ⓓ a place where Lucie wants to live all the time

4. Lucie learns to like Mrs. Tiggy-Winkle. But she will not sit close to Mrs. Tiggy-Winkle. Why?

Ⓐ She is angry at Mrs. Tiggy-Winkle for stealing her things.

Ⓑ She does not like to talk very much.

Ⓒ Mrs. Tiggy-Winkle's spines hurt.

Ⓓ Mrs. Tiggy-Winkle is so sore and tired.

5. At the end of the story, the reader finds out that Mrs. Tiggy-Winkle is really a

Ⓐ pig.

Ⓑ porcupine.

Ⓒ hog.

Ⓓ hedgehog.

For the open-ended questions, remember to:
- **Focus your response on the question asked.**
- **Answer all parts of the question.**
- **Give a complete explanation.**
- **Use specific information from the directions.**

---

6. Think about the job that Mrs. Tiggy-Winkle performs for a living. The author never says exactly what it is. What is the job? How do you know what it is? Use details from the story to support your answer.

The job Mrs. Tiggy Winkle does
is a cleaner with clothing.
Also with other stuff like handkerchiss
and other Items. Also she returns
them.

7. **Which of the creatures best shows what Mrs. Tiggy-Winkle looks like? Circle it. Using the lines below, explain why you think this is the best choice. Use details from the story.**

I think it is the dark Pitcher of the hedgehog. Because the animal in the story sounds just like it. Also she had spines. Also she is very tiny. And they drank tea.

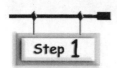

Step 1

Set your purpose for reading.

WHAT ARE EVERYDAY TEXTS?

Directions Read the paragraph. Answer the questions that follow.

The things you read each day, like signs and posters, are called **everyday text.** Some everyday texts help to explain ideas, like the ones you read in magazines and in newspapers. Everyday text can also be the commercials and shows you see on television and the movies you watch.

1. What kinds of everyday text do you read?

    _____

    _____

    _____

2. What kinds of everyday text do you watch?

    _____

    _____

    _____

Sometimes written text will have pictures to help you understand what you read. For example, a newspaper article that has pictures might help you learn what is happening to people in other parts of the world.

Everyday text, like this workbook, can also give directions. It provides directions for reading, writing, listening, viewing, and speaking. Directions can also be found on packages of food and directions for games, tools, and machines. What kinds of projects have you completed by following directions?

Directions Look at the pictures. Answer the questions or follow the directions below the pictures.

1. Which picture shows a box that would have directions? Draw a circle around this thing.

2. Read the words that are part of this picture. Think about what is described by these words. What kinds of things would you find inside the box?

_____

_____

3. Think about the kind of directions that would be on the box. What would the directions help readers to do?

_____

_____

4. Which picture shows something that includes stories? Draw a box around this picture.

5. Study the title in this picture. What kind of articles would be found in this everyday text?

_____

_____

6. Read the words that are part of this picture. What game is named on this cover?

_____

_____

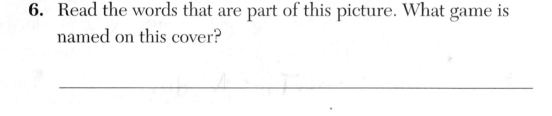

HOW ARE EVERYDAY TEXTS PUT TOGETHER?

Step 2

Recognize the organizational structure of the text.

Directions Read the paragraph. Answer the questions that follow.

Reading every day helps you become a good reader. Practice by reading aloud. Ask yourself questions as you read. For example: How is this text like another that I have already read? How are the ideas alike? How are they different? What message is the author trying to give me? Answering questions like these can also help you as you study mathematics, science, and social studies.

1. Look at a lesson from one of your schoolbooks. Read the title and headings. What one thing or idea is the lesson about?

   _____

   _____

2. What have you learned about the subject just by reading the title and headings?

   _____

   _____

   _____

3. Look at a chapter in a nonfiction book from the library. Read the title and headings. What one thing or idea is the chapter about?

   _____

   _____

4. What have you learned about the subject of the book just by reading the title and headings?

   _____

   _____

   _____

Directions Read the paragraphs. Answer the questions that follow.

As you learned before, everyday text can do many different things. Some might explain ideas. Some might describe events. Whatever is being explained or described, it is important to know that each text has just one **main idea** about the **topic.** This means that all the information and details the author writes in the text help to explain that topic.

An author presents this information in **sentences.** Together, all the sentences combine into **paragraphs** that help the author describe his or her main idea about a topic.

OTHER TEXT STRUCTURES

Cause and Effect

You may have heard the saying "Things happen for a reason." The reason something happens is called the **cause.** What happens next, or because of it, is the **effect.** One effect can even lead to another action. All these actions help explain a message or main idea. For example, in science, causes and effects may tell you how a molecule is put together. The same causes and effects also tell how molecules work together.

A set of directions can include causes and effects. They explain why you must do certain tasks in a certain order. This way you learn how the tasks link together to create something. When you are asked to follow a set of directions, look for causes and effects. They will help you understand what to do and why.

1. When a baseball player hits a ball, what happens to the ball?

_____

2. When a bowling ball rolls down the lane and hits a pin, what is the effect?

_____

Directions Read the paragraphs. Answer the questions that follow.

Fact and Opinion

Facts are details that are true. It means the details can be proved. Everyday texts will often present facts about many topics. These facts explain or describe a topic. Sometimes authors include their **opinions.** These are the author's own ideas, feelings, and beliefs. Opinions are not always true.

A social studies or history book often tells facts about the past. You may also learn about opinions held by people who lived back then. As you read, you will also learn how the author feels about this time in history.

1. Your local newspaper gives the score of a little-league hockey game. Is the score a fact or an opinion? Why?

    _____

    _____

    _____

2. A game box says: "You are guaranteed to have a lot of fun!" Is this a fact or an opinion?

    _____

    _____

Directions Find a partner and look at the pictures. Talk about the details shown in the pictures. List important ideas about the pictures. Write these ideas in the chart on the next page.

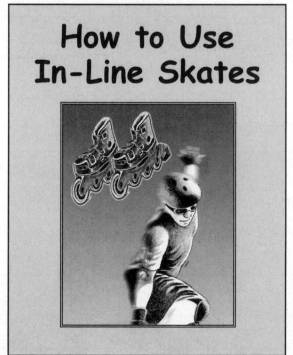

Everyday Text Study Guide

Which picture shows something that tells a story? _____ _____	Which picture shows something that would include directions? _____ _____
What does the title tell you about the topic of this movie? _____ _____	What does the title tell you about the topic of this book? _____ _____
What do you think the main idea might be? _____ _____	What do you think the main idea might be? _____ _____
What details do you learn by studying the picture? _____ _____ _____	What details do you learn by studying the book's cover? _____ _____ _____
What causes and effects might you learn by watching this movie? _____ _____ _____	What causes and effects might you learn by reading this book? _____ _____ _____
Think about the things that might happen in this movie. What might people feel as they watch this movie? _____ _____	Think about the way that in-line skates are used. What might authors want people to feel as they read the directions? _____ _____

Step 3

Understand the author's purpose and the reader's purpose.

HOW DO AUTHORS PRESENT FACTS AND DIRECTIONS?

Authors write for a **purpose.** Sometimes, everyday texts are written to inform. The author wants the reader to learn about a topic. For example, a newspaper article might be about a fire that burned a building. The reader will learn about how the fire started. It might also be about a firefighter who became a hero. The reporter makes a point, or **main idea,** about the topic.

HOW DO READERS USE EVERYDAY TEXTS?

As a reader, your purpose is to understand the main idea. For instance, it is important to read all the directions for something before following the steps. This will help you learn the author's purpose. Find the topic as you skim a set of directions and decide on the main idea. Think about the details included by the author. It may help to read aloud and answer questions like the **5Ws and H:** *who, what, where, when, why,* and *how.* Use the answers to write a **summary**. Then you will have all the facts you need to understand and carry out these directions.

Examine all kinds of texts to help improve your own writing. Identify interesting ways of stating ideas. Look for new ways of organizing and presenting main ideas and **supporting details.** Find answers to the following questions. How are causes and effects presented? Which ideas are facts? Which ideas are opinions? How do the author's opinions help support the main idea? Take notes of features that interest you. Remember to use these notes when you complete writing projects.

Step 4

Study charts, graphs, and diagrams to see what information they present.

Sometimes, everyday texts have special pictures or **graphics.** They help you understand the topic and supporting ideas. You can also use details from charts, graphs, and diagrams to study new words.

WHAT ARE CHARTS?

Charts show important information and ideas in rows and columns. There are many different kinds of charts, but all charts have **headings** that provide information and details about what is being shown. The details might be words, phrases, sentences, or even numbers.

Directions Look at the chart below. Study the facts that are listed. Answer the questions that follow.

Bodies of Water in New Jersey

Rivers	Lakes
Hudson River	Lake Hopatcong
Delaware River	Lake Mohawk
Passaic River	Budd Lake

1. Read the chart's title. What will you learn by reading this chart?

   We are learning about
   Attendance

2. Study the heading of the left-hand column. What kinds of facts and details will be listed in this column?

3. Study the heading of the right-hand column. What kinds of facts and details will be listed in this column?

_____

_____

4. Read the list of details under the heading "Rivers." What are three rivers found in New Jersey?

_____

_____

_____

5. Read the list of details under the heading "Lakes." What are three lakes found in New Jersey?

_____

_____

_____

WHAT ARE GRAPHS?

Graphs also show important ideas. Like charts, there are many different kinds of graphs. One kind shows information in rows and columns. **Bar graphs** help show how quantities are different from each other. **Line graphs** show how quantities change over time. These details may help an author show what he or she is trying to say about a topic.

Directions Look at the graph below. Study the facts that are listed. Answer the questions that follow.

Number of Pupils Who Have Perfect Attendance

3rd Grade	🏅🏅🏅🏅🏅🏅🏅🏅🏅🏅
4th Grade	🏅🏅🏅🏅🏅
5th Grade	🏅🏅🏅🏅🏅🏅🏅
6th Grade	🏅🏅🏅

KEY

🏅 each medal represents 10 pupils.

1. Read the graph's title. What will you learn by reading this graph?

   We are learning about perfect Attendance.

2. Look at the key for the graph. What does each medal stand for?

   each one stands for 6

3. How many medals are beside the heading "6th Grade"?

   3th grad 3.

4. If each medal stands for ten pupils, how many 6th-grade pupils have perfect attendance?

   30 people

5. Count the number of medals in each row. Which row has the highest number of medals?

   3rd Graded

6. What do these ten medals tell you about the pupils in this grade?

   3rd Grade have hire attendance
   then other grades.

WHAT ARE DIAGRAMS?

A **diagram** is a picture that can do a number of things. For example, a diagram can show you all the parts of something. Each part is named. A diagram can also help you understand how something works. Directions use diagrams to show how the steps are done.

Directions Look at the diagram below. Study the descriptions and facts that are shown. Then read the instructions for each sentence.

A Personal Computer

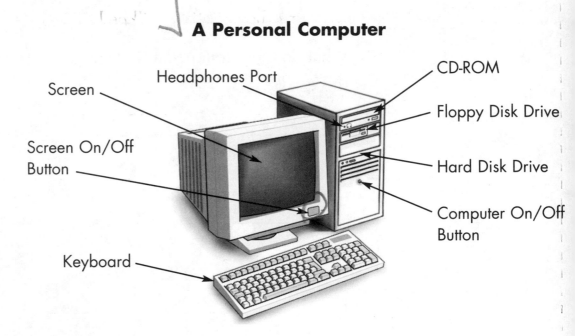

Screen

Headphones Port

CD-ROM

Floppy Disk Drive

Screen On/Off Button

Hard Disk Drive

Computer On/Off Button

Keyboard

1. Place a check mark beside the title of this diagram.

2. Color the computer screen red.

3. Circle the button that turns the computer on.

4. Color the keyboard blue.

5. Color the disk drive orange.

6. Draw an X on the floppy disk drive.

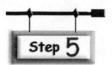

Step 5

Put your prereading skills together as you prepare to read.

Directions Answer the following questions.

1. You will read a set of directions called "Crystal Creations." It is from an Internet site called *Science Explorer.* What do you think the directions will be like?

_____

_____

2. What do you think can be made by following these directions?

_____

3. What kinds of things will you probably learn by reading these directions?

_____

_____

_____

4. How will you learn what the topic of this selection is? How will you learn the author's purpose?

_____

_____

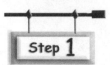

Step 1

Use skills to read and/or listen to whole texts.

You are about to read a set of directions and answer questions about it. Write your answers on the Problem and Solution Chart that your teacher will give you. The questions will help you to:

- understand the purpose of the everyday text
- name causes and effects, distinguish facts from opinions, and identify main ideas and supporting details
- use pictures and diagrams to understand the steps in the directions
- use questions to examine the directions
- make decisions about the ideas that are presented
- summarize the directions
- draw your own ideas about the text and its details
- and read independently

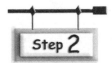

Step 2

Study important words from the story.

The following words are used in the story you are about to read. Read each word and think about its meaning. Look for the words as you read the story. Think about how each word is used in the story.

shallow—not deep
dissolved—melted
evaporates—dries up
chemically—in the way that atoms and molecules are made

Step 3

Use word skills to increase your vocabulary.

WHAT ARE SOME TOOLS FOR LEARNING NEW WORDS?

Whenever you read you will see new words every time—in stories, newspapers, magazines, directions, and even when you surf the Internet. You will also hear new words as you watch TV or movies and listen to the radio. **Vocabulary** tools help you learn how to say new words, what they mean, and how to use them in your own writing and speaking. Begin by looking up the words in a dictionary or glossary. Here are some other strategies to use while you are reading.

Whenever you read a new word, try using these vocabulary strategies to help you figure it out and understand its meaning.

Decide how to say the word

When you see a word that is new to you, try saying it out loud. You can often figure out how to say a word, and get the word's meaning, by linking letters to the sounds they stand for. This is a good way to **pronounce,** or "sound out," the word. Sounding out words helps because you may recognize the word once you hear it.

When you try to **decode,** or figure out, an unknown word, look for **patterns.** Notice **phonograms,** or groups of letters, that you know. This is especially helpful with long words. Try dividing longer words into **syllables,** or the sounds made by one or more letters in a word.

Find the parts that make up a compound word

A **root** is a word part that contains the word's basic meaning. Prefixes and suffixes are added to the root to change its meaning or part of speech.

Sometimes a root can be a word that stands by itself. For example, **act + -or** is **actor. King + -dom** is **kingdom.**

A root can also be a word part that comes from Latin or Greek. Usually, these roots cannot stand by themselves. For example, the root **bio-** in the word **biography** is not a word.

A **prefix** is a word part that is added *before* a word or word root and changes the word's meaning.

A **suffix** is a word part that is added *after* a word or word root and changes the word's meaning.

Decide how the word fits in its context

A sentence has its own **structure. Word order** is the order of words in a sentence. **Simple sentences** are made up of a **subject** followed by a **predicate.**

Another way to figure out the meaning of a word is to look for clues in the words, sentences, or even paragraphs that come before and after it. When you see a word you do not know, the **context** will sometimes tell you its meaning.

Directions   Read each paragraph below. Say the underlined word or words aloud. Study the meaning of each sentence. Write a definition for the word without using a dictionary or a glossary. Then when you are finished, use a dictionary or glossary to check your work.

1. Sherri wasn't feeling well. Her mother took her to see Dr. Nighthorse, who then sent Sherri for <u>lab work</u>. These tests showed that Sherri had strep throat. Sherri's mom made sure that she got medicine, plenty of rest, and that she drank lots of water. In a week, Sherri was as good as new.

   _____

   _____

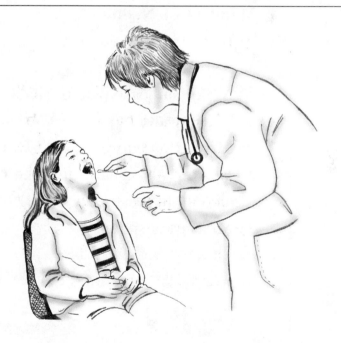

2. Our picnic looked yummy. There was one problem. We had plastic forks and spoons, but in our hurry, we had left the <u>dinnerware</u> at home. Then Dad had a great idea. We had plenty of paper cups. We could each use two or three cups. It would be simple to eat out of them.

   _____

   _____

READING WITH COMPREHENSION

Guided Reading Instruction

Step 4

Understand stories by identifying point of view, facts from opinions, and main idea and supporting details.

Reading Guide	Guided Questions

Directions   Put it all together. Use all the strategies you have learned so far. They will help you read "Crystal Creations." Look at the questions and comments on the side. They will help improve your comprehension of this set of directions.

❶
> Crystal Creations
> Grow Spikes of Crystals in the Sun
> *—The Science Explorer*

❶ What does the title tell you about this set of directions?

❷ **What Do I Need?**
- Black construction paper
- Scissors
- A pie pan, cake pan, or shallow bowl
- Warm water
- Measuring cup
- Epsom salt (usually near the rubbing alcohol in the supermarket)
- Measuring spoons

❷ How will this list help you carry out the directions? How do the pictures help you understand the list?

Reading Guide

❸ **Tips for Home Scientists:** This activity works best on a sunny day.

❹ **1.** Use your scissors to cut the black paper so it will fit in the bottom of your pie pan.

2. Add 1 tablespoon of Epsom salt to 1/4 cup of warm water. Stir until the salt is dissolved.

❺ **3.** Pour the salty water onto the black paper in the pie pan.

4. Put the pie pan out into the sun.

❻ **5.** When the water evaporates, you'll see lots of crystal spikes on the black paper!

The Mudd family discovered that these crystals look great under a microscope.

Guided Questions

❸ Why will the tip help people do the experiment correctly?

❹ How does the author show the order in which the steps must be done? Why are the pictures important?

❺ What must be done before the water is poured into the pan or bowl?

❻ How does the sun affect the experiment?

Reading Guide

Why does Epsom salt make crystal spikes?

❼ When you add Epsom salt to water, the salt dissolves. When you leave the pan in the sun, the water evaporates and the salt forms crystals shaped like long needles.

❽ If you tried this experiment with table salt instead of Epsom salt, you wouldn't get crystal spikes. That's because table salt and Epsom salt are chemically different, so the crystals that they form are very different.

❾ The picture below shows part of an artwork created for the Exploratorium by Swiss artist Jörg Lenzlinger. He mixed different kinds of salts with water. As the water evaporated, the salts crystallized, making beautiful shapes that kept growing and changing.

Guided Questions

❼ Read the paragraph. How does it help you with the meaning of the word *spikes*. What does the word mean in this context?

❽ What can cause the experiment not to work?

❾ What is the main idea of this article?

Directions   Use details from the everyday text you just read to answer the following questions. Fill in the circle beside the answer that you choose.

1. **What are the scissors used for?**

   Ⓐ   to cut the construction paper

   Ⓑ   to make the bowl shallow

   Ⓒ   to open the Epsom salt

   Ⓓ   to cut the crystals apart

2. **Why is the note about Epsom salt included?**

   Ⓐ   to explain how Epsom salt are different from table salt

   Ⓑ   to show that Epsom salt can cause injury

   Ⓒ   to show what can be used in place of Epsom salt

   Ⓓ   to help people find Epsom salt in a store

3. **What tool can be used to see tiny details that make up the crystals?**

   Ⓐ   warm water

   Ⓑ   bright sunlight

   Ⓒ   a microscope

   Ⓓ   a camera

4. **Why is black construction paper placed on the bottom of the bowl?**

   Ⓐ   so that the water does not dry up

   Ⓑ   so that the salt crystals show up and are easy to see

   Ⓒ   so that the Epsom salt will mix with the water

   Ⓓ   so that the water will not leak

5. **Why is the weather important in doing this experiment successfully?**

   Ⓐ   If the weather is too cold, the crystals will sink to the bottom of the bowl.

   Ⓑ   If the room is too hot, the Epsom salt will dry up before it can be mixed with the water.

   Ⓒ   If the day is not sunny, the water might dry up slowly or not dry up at all.

   Ⓓ   If the day is rainy, the bowl will fill up with too much water.

For the open-ended questions, remember to:
- **Focus your response on the question asked.**
- **Answer all parts of the question.**
- **Give a complete explanation.**
- **Use specific information from the directions.**

---

6. **Look at the picture on page 42. Why do you think the artist used different kinds of salts to create his artwork? Explain how the artwork was made. Write about the way in which Epsom salt and table salt are alike and how they are different. Describe how science information helped the artist.**

   Use details from the selection to support your answer. Write your answer on the lines below.

   _____

   _____

   _____

   _____

   _____

7. How do the text and its pictures help you understand the meaning of a new word? Choose one word from the set of directions. Describe how the word parts or context help readers understand the word.

Use details from the selection to support your answer. Write your answer on the lines below.

_____

_____

_____

_____

_____

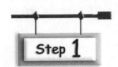

Step 1

Set a purpose for your reading.

WHAT IS INFORMATIONAL TEXT?

It is important to read all different kinds of texts every day. This practice helps you develop your reading skills. **Informational text** is **nonfiction**. It tells about true events and presents facts about a topic. You read this kind of information in your textbooks every day. For example, you learn about real people, places, things, and events.

Nonfiction can come in many printed forms. Here are some general examples:

A **textbook** is a book you use in school to study a particular subject. For example, you may have a textbook for social studies and another one for mathematics.

A **biography** is the story of a person's life that is written by someone else. An **autobiography** is the story of a person's life that is also written by that person.

An **interview** is a formal talk with a person. One person asks questions. This person is called the interviewer. Another person answers the questions. This person is the subject of the interview.

A **magazine article** is usually a short piece of writing. It tells you information about a topic. For example, you may read a magazine article about animals in the wild or about how artists use computers.

Today, technology is all around us. **Technical information** gives us facts and details about the machines and equipment we use. For example, you might read technical information about how your computer works.

Directions Look at the pictures. Then answer the questions or follow the instructions for each sentence.

1. One picture shows something that is not real. Circle this picture.

2. Study the picture. How do you know this is not something that is real?

_____

3. One picture shows something that can happen in real life. Draw a box around this picture.

4. Study the picture. How is this picture like real life?

_____

_____

5. Write a sentence in your own words that tells what you think is happening in this picture.

_____

_____

Step 2

Recognize the organizational structure of the texts that you read.

WHAT MAKES UP INFORMATIONAL TEXT?

What will you find in informational text? The main idea is what the author wants you to know about a topic. Informational text also includes supporting details. The author uses these facts and details to explain or describe the topic. These details also help support the point that the author is making. Studying supporting details will help you discover the main idea of a piece of informational text.

Directions Look at the picture and read the paragraphs. Then read the numbered sentences. Follow the instructions for each sentence.

Have you ever seen an anthill? I bet you never looked inside. The hill covers a hole that leads to tunnels the ants have dug under the ground. Each tunnel ends in a room. Ants pile up food in some of these rooms.

The leader of the ants is the queen. She is also the biggest ant in the anthill. The queen ant is very important because she lays all the eggs that will become baby ants. The other rooms in the anthill will make homes for the baby ants. Anthills are one of the wonders of the world!

1. Read the first sentence again. Circle the word that tells the topic of this paragraph.

2. What is the purpose of an anthill? Fill in the circle beside the answer that you choose.
   - (A) place where ants grow food
   - (B) place where ants eat the food
   - (C) place where ants live and store food
   - (D) place where only the queen ant lives

3. Which is NOT part of an anthill? Fill in the circle beside the answer that you choose.
   - (A) grass
   - (B) food storage rooms
   - (C) rooms where ants live
   - (D) tunnels

4. Look at the picture and reread the second paragraph. Which ant is the most important in the anthill? Circle this ant.

5. Underline the details that helped you decide which ant is the most important.

6. Which sentence is the main idea for the second paragraph? Fill in the circle beside the answer that you choose.
   - (A) Not all anthills are the same.
   - (B) An anthill is an amazing place.
   - (C) It takes no time for ants to build an anthill.
   - (D) People should build homes like anthills.

NONFICTION TEXT STRUCTURES

End Punctuation	These are **periods**(.), **question marks**(?), and **exclamation points**(!). When you see each one, you know you have reached the end of a sentence.
Paragraphs	A **paragraph** is a group of sentences. All the sentences are about one idea or a point the writer is trying to make.
Cause and Effect	One event may be the reason another event happens. The first event is the **cause**. The second event is the **effect**.
Fact and Opinion	Ideas that can be proved are *facts*. For example, it is a fact that the sun sets in the west each evening. An author's feelings and beliefs are **opinions**. An author's opinion might be that sunset is a sad time of day.
Conclusion	The **conclusion** is a **summary** that comes at the end. It usually repeats the main idea. An author may finish in different ways. The author may end by stating the main idea again. The author may sum up all the details. Both ways help drive a point home and help make it stronger.

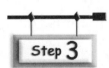

Step 3

Understand the author's purpose and the reader's purpose.

HOW DO AUTHORS AND READERS USE INFORMATION FROM TEXTS?

Every author states a **main idea.** This is the point the author makes about a topic. Making this point is called the **author's purpose**.

There is a purpose for the reader, too. A reader must make a decision about the text by thinking about the facts and opinions an author presents. As a reader you should use these ideas to **draw conclusions**. It will help you decide about the topic and the author's main idea. It will also help you to notice the ways in which authors use different words and what context they use them in. How will this help to improve your own writing?

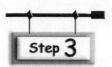

Step 3

Understand the
author's purpose
and the
reader's purpose.

HOW ARE GRAPHIC ORGANIZERS USED?

There are many different kinds of graphic organizers—charts, graphs, idea webs, Venn diagrams and so on. Look at the examples below:

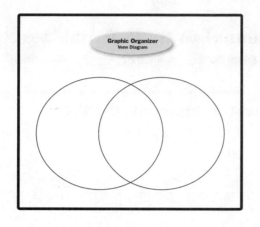

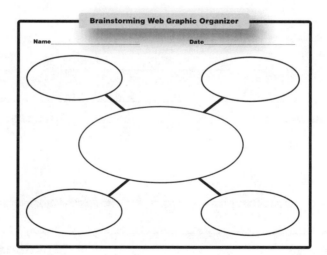

In this lesson, you will learn how to use one that will help you study nonfiction text while you are reading.

When you begin reading, try to notice the author's topic. You may not notice it right away, but finding it is an important first step in your understanding the author's purpose. After that, find all the important details and main ideas that back up the topic. Try using the **5Ws** and **H**: *who, what, where, when, why,* and *how.* When the chart is complete, you will have a good amount of details about the point the author is trying to make.

Directions Find a partner and choose an ad from a newspaper or magazine. Take turns reading it aloud to each other. List the important ideas about the ad. Write these ideas in the chart below.

Informational Graphic Organizer

Statement that presents the topic

Reasons	Supporting Details

Causes	Effects

Facts	Opinions

Conclusion

Step 4

Put your
prereading skills
together as you
prepare to read.

Directions Answer the following questions.

1. You will read "The Moon Landing Hoax" by Gil Knier and
Becky Bray It is an informational article from *NASA Kids*
magazine. What kinds of informational texts might the
magazine contain?

_____

2. What will be the topics of these informational texts?

_____

_____

3. Study the title. Think about what informational text is like.
What are some facts that you would expect to find in
this article?

_____

_____

4. How will you learn what the topic and the author's purpose are?

_____

_____

5. What kind of pictures do you expect to see in an article
about space and the space program?

_____

_____

Use skills to read and/or listen to whole texts.

You are about to read an informational selection and answer questions about it. Write your answers on the Cause and Effect T-Chart that your teacher will give you. They will help you to:

● understand the purpose of the informational text
● recognize causes and effects, distinguish facts from opinions, and identify main ideas and supporting details
● use pictures and diagrams to understand the ideas in informational text
● use questions to examine informational texts
● make decisions about the science ideas that are presented
● summarize informational text
● draw your own ideas about informational text and its details
● read independently

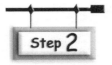

Study important words from the story.

You will need to know the following words for the story. Read each word and think about its meaning. Look for the words as you read the informational article. Think about how each word is used in the article.

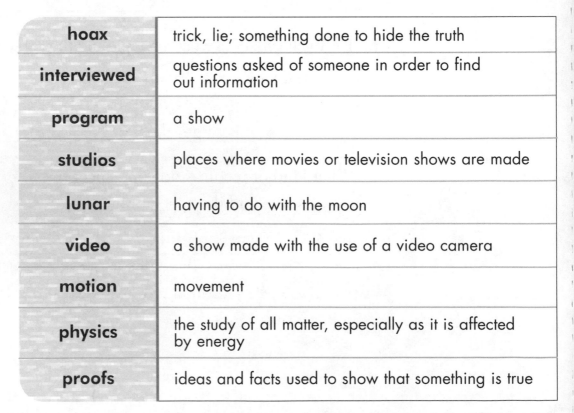

hoax	trick, lie; something done to hide the truth
interviewed	questions asked of someone in order to find out information
program	a show
studios	places where movies or television shows are made
lunar	having to do with the moon
video	a show made with the use of a video camera
motion	movement
physics	the study of all matter, especially as it is affected by energy
proofs	ideas and facts used to show that something is true

convincing	believable
unique	totally new or different
public	all people
researchers	people who carry out special studies
challenged	to have questioned the truth about a happening or idea
engineers	people who study and design machines
ingenious	very clever and able to solve very difficult problems

Step 3

Use word skills to increase your vocabulary.

WHAT ARE SOME TOOLS FOR LEARNING NEW WORDS?

Whenever you read a new word, try using these vocabulary strategies to help you figure it out and understand its meaning.

Decide how to say the word

Try to **pronounce**, or "sound out," the word. Remember that **letters** stand for **sounds**. Sometimes you can figure out how to say a difficult word, and get the word's meaning, by linking sounds to letters. Then, when you hear it again, you will recognize it.

Look for familiar **patterns** when you try to figure out an unknown word. Notice **phonograms**, or groups of letters, that you know. This is especially helpful with long words. Try dividing longer words into **syllables**, or the sounds made by one or more letters in a word.

There are some important kinds of words to watch out for when you are decoding and figuring out word context:

A **homograph** is one of two or more words that are spelled alike but have different meanings or even different pronunciations. For example, the *bow* of a ship and a *bow* and arrow.

A **homophone** is one of two or more words that are pronounced alike but have different meanings or even spellings. A good example of this is the words to, too, and two.

Find the parts that make up a compound word

A **root** is a word part that contains the word's basic meaning. Other word parts can be added to the root to change its meaning or part of speech. A **prefix** is a word part that is added *before* a word or word root and changes the word's meaning. A **suffix** is a word part that is added *after* a word or word root and changes the word's meaning.

Sometimes a root can be a word that stands by itself. For example, **sub- + marine** is submarine. **Foot + ball** is **football**.

A root can also be a word part that comes from Latin or Greek. Usually, these roots cannot stand by themselves. For example, the root **bio-** in the word **biography** is not a word.

Decide how the word fits in its context.

A sentence has its own **structure**. **Word order** is the order of words in a sentence. **Simple sentences** are made up of a **subject** followed by a **predicate**.

Another way to figure out the meaning of a word is to look for clues in the words, sentences, or even paragraphs that come before and after it. When you see a word you do not know, the **context** will sometimes tell you its meaning.

Directions Read each paragraph below. Say the underlined word aloud. Study the meaning of each sentence. Write a definition for the word. Use a dictionary or glossary to check your work.

1. Soldana was pleased with her mathematics test. There were some inaccuracies, but there were far more accuracies. In fact, Soldana's mistakes only brought her grade down from an A to a B. She knew she would not miss a single problem next time.

    _____

    _____

2. Our mountain climbing trip was a little frightening at first. But we had the hang of climbing in no time at all. At noon we stopped for lunch. Our picnic area was a large flat boulder. You could see for miles from that huge stone on the side of the mountain. Everyone was much bolder now. We all walked right up to the edge with no fear at all!

    _____

    _____

Guided Reading Instruction

Step 4

Understand informational text by identifying cause and effect, fact from opinions, and main idea and supporting details.

READING WITH COMPREHENSION

Reading Guide	Guided Questions

Directions Put it all together now. Use the strategies you have learned so far. They will help you read "The Moon Landing Hoax." Look at the questions and comments on the side. They will help improve your comprehension of this example of informational text.

1

The Moon Landing Hoax
from NASA Kids website

2 Did we actually send humans to the Moon in the 1960's? Of course we did! But some people are claiming that NASA lied about it. They think we faked the landings. Actually, it would have been harder to fake the whole thing than it was to do it! But many people are confused about it, and have asked NASA to clear it up.

The confusion began with a TV program called *Conspiracy Theory: Did We Land on the Moon*? The program interviewed people who didn't think NASA knew how to make it to the Moon. They thought that the USA wanted to beat the Soviet Union to the Moon so much that we used movie studios to pretend we were going! But not only did they think NASA faked the whole thing; they thought we couldn't even do the fake well! These people on *Conspiracy Theory* said there were a lot of "errors." **3 4** Well, let's look at a couple of them:

1 The title raises an important question. What part of the moon landing was a hoax, or trick? Read the informational text to find out.

2 What will the authors tell about the hoax?

3 Why did people believe that there really was a moon landing hoax?

4 What will the sentences in this article tell about the moon landing hoax?

Reading Guide	Guided Questions

Stars in the Lunar Sky

Pictures of astronauts sent from the Moon don't include stars in the dark lunar sky. How could that be? Did NASA's film makers forget to turn on the stars? Most people who take photos know the answer: It's hard to take a picture of something very bright and something else very dim on the same photo. Ever watch a TV program or movie with outdoor scenes? Next time you see one, look for stars in the sky. You won't see them because they are just too dim for the camera to see. **5 6**

5 Look at the word *dim*. Now look for the context clues that tell you about it. What does the word *dim* mean?

A Waving Flag

Everyone has seen the video of astronauts planting a US flag on the Moon. You can see the flag bending and rippling. How can that be? There's no breeze on the Moon to move the flag. Well, when the astronauts planted the flag they twisted it back and forth to get it into the soil. On the Earth, that would have made the flag "wave" for a few seconds, then stop. But that's because on Earth the flag pushes against air as it flaps, and the air slows it down. On the Moon, there was no air to stop the flag's motion. So it continued, just as Newton's First Law of physics says it should. So of course the cloth flag waved back and forth under the metal rod holding it. **7**

6 Stars cannot be seen in shows about moon landings. What details do the authors present to prove this is correct?

7 There is no air on the moon. What do scientists think caused the flag to "wave"?

8 How does the photograph support ideas explained in the article?

Reading Guide

The TV show had plenty of other "proofs," but they are all just as easy to disprove. **9** But another answer is: just plain common sense.

For instance, Russia, China, East Germany and other countries were very unfriendly toward the USA at that time. They watched everything we did very closely. It was easy to tell whether the Apollo radio signals were coming from the direction of the Moon. If anything had seemed wrong, these unfriendly countries would certainly have told the world that the USA was pulling a hoax! Yet none of them ever questioned NASA's success. When even your enemy gives you credit for something, it's pretty convincing!

There is also 841 pounds of proof: the Moon rocks Apollo astronauts brought home to Earth. The rocks are very different from Earth rocks.

"Moon rocks are truly unique, and differ from Earth rocks in many ways," says Dr. David McKay of NASA's Johnson Space Center. David works at NASA's Lunar Sample Laboratory Facility where most of the Moon rocks are stored. "Several museums, such as the Smithsonian and others, let the public touch and examine rocks from the Moon," says David.

David says that faking a Moon rock to fool scientists around the world would be next to impossible. "It would be far easier to just go to the Moon and get one!" he says. **10**

"Researchers in hundreds of labs have examined Apollo Moon samples—and not one of them has ever challenged where the rocks came from! These are not NASA people, either—but are scientists in dozens of countries to whom I loaned Moon rock samples." **11**

Guided Questions

9 Look at the word disprove. Using what you know about suffixes, and other vocabulary strategies, what does the word disprove mean?

10 What is Dr. David McKay's opinion about faking a moon rock?

11 Think about the moon rocks. What are the opinions of many world scientists about these rocks?

Reading Guide

There are other common-sense reasons to believe NASA sent men to the Moon. Nine of the twelve men who walked on the Moon are still alive, and are honest, believable men. And NASA would have had to include many, many engineers in the hoax. Those engineers were just regular people, doing an exciting job. Would every single person be willing to go along with the trickery, and lie about it for 30 years? **12** We're sure no *NASA Kids* would!

The *Conspiracy Theory* program is fun to watch, but be sure to not believe it! The hardworking, ingenious Americans who got us to the Moon should be honored for their success and their pioneering spirit. Even though the job of exploring space has been handed on to a younger generation of engineers, we are all proud of what NASA has done. **13**

Guided Questions

12 What is the authors' opinion about the people who work for NASA?

13 Do you think the moon landings were real? What details from the article support your opinion?

**NJ ASK
Practice**

Directions Use details from the informational article to answer the following questions. Fill in the circle beside the answer that you choose.

1. **A theory is an idea that might be true. It must be backed up with reasons. What part of the article do the authors say is a theory?**

   Ⓐ that the TV program was nonfiction

   Ⓑ that the moon rocks are real

   Ⓒ that *NASA Kids* believe the moon landings did not happen

   Ⓓ that the moon landings were a hoax

2. **According to the article, which is NOT a reason some people believe the moon landing was a hoax?**

   Ⓐ No stars can be seen in pictures of the moon landing.

   Ⓑ There are no pictures of the astronauts flying to the moon.

   Ⓒ Air makes the flag wave, and there is no air on the moon.

   Ⓓ NASA didn't know how to make it to the moon.

3. **How do the authors show that the ideas of the TV show are not true?**

   Ⓐ by getting the TV people to admit they were lying

   Ⓑ by showing that only people outside the United States believe the moon landings were a hoax

   Ⓒ by using science to show why stars can't be seen and the flag does wave

   Ⓓ by showing how badly the TV show's pictures were made

4. **Whose ideas help NASA prove that the moon landings happened?**

   Ⓐ scientists from many countries

   Ⓑ editors at *NASA Kids*

   Ⓒ people who run space radios

   Ⓓ workers in museums

5. **What do the authors want readers to use in thinking about the moon landings?**

Ⓒ new telescopes

ⓑ reading skills

ⓒ common sense

ⓖ personal beliefs

For the open-ended questions, remember to:
- Focus your response on the question asked.
- Answer all parts of the question.
- Give a complete explanation.
- Use specific information from the directions.

---

6. **Do you think that the article's ideas follow common sense? What details strongly support the idea that the moon landings really did happen? Describe how science helps explain away the mistaken opinions some people have about the moon landings. Find details that helped you form opinions about the moon landings.**

Use details from the informational selection to support your answers. Write your answers on the lines below.

_____

_____

_____

_____

_____

_____

7. Why do you think it is important for NASA to prove
   that the moon landings really happened? Explain
   how the ideas from Conspiracy Theory would make
   the people at NASA feel. Describe what would
   happen to the American space program if it was
   found to be dishonest.

   Use details from the informational selection to
   support your answer.

   _____

   _____

   _____

   _____

   _____

   _____

**Focus
on the
New Jersey
CCCS**

**Guided
Instruction**

Step 1

Set a purpose
for your
reading.

WHAT IS A POEM?

A **poem** is a form of writing that expresses a strong feeling or tells a story in a very few words. A poem is often lovely to hear, like music. A poem might have **rhythm** and **rhyme**. Rhythm is the beat of the lines that gives a poem its musical sound. Rhyme is when words at the end of lines sound the same.

A poem can sometimes seem hard to read. Try reading it slowly and silently to yourself the first time. Concentrate on what each word means. Then try reading the poem aloud. Pay attention to the **punctuation** in each **stanza**, or the lines in a poem that are grouped together. It will help you read aloud successfully. When you're finished, ask yourself, "What is the poet saying about life? Does the poem give me a lesson about life?"

Directions   Read the poem. Answer the questions that follow.

When Whales Exhale
(Whale Watching)
—*Constance Levy*

1	There's a horn sound
2	from the blowhole
3	and a high-speed spout
4	when a whale at sea
5	blasts the old air out.
6	It breathes up a geyser,
7	a flare of fizz,
8	a white cloud that shows you
9	where it is
10	in the endless waves
11	of the great green sea.
12	Oh, whales exhale
13	magnificently.

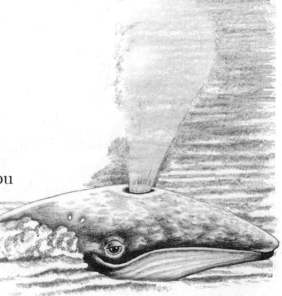

1. Read the title. What animal is the main character in this poem? Circle this word in the title.

2. Line 1 begins with a word that is capitalized. Which line ends this sentence with a period?

   line five

3. The words between the capitalized word and the period are the first sentence of the poem. How many lines make up this sentence?

   5 lines.

4. How many sentences make up the whole poem?

   3

5. The word *magnificently* means *beautifully*. What does this word tell you about the poet's opinion of the way whales breathe?

   The poits thinks that wales are beaitisul. Also amasing.

Step 2

Recognize the organizational structure of the texts that you read.

WHAT ARE THE DIFFERENT TYPES OF POETRY?

On the New Jersey ASK Language Arts Literacy test you may read a poem. Then you will answer questions and write about the poem you've read. The kinds of poems you might see include **narrative poems** and **lyric poems**.

Narrative Poems

A **narrative poem** tells a story. It features a plot, or a series of things that happen. Usually the story is told in the order in which events happened. Did you know that Dr. Seuss's *How the Grinch Stole Christmas* is a narrative poem?

Lyric Poems

A **lyric poem** gives the thoughts and feelings of the poet. There is no story or series of events. Instead, there is usually a description of something. It might be something in nature, like a dolphin or a thunderstorm. It might be an emotion, like happiness or sadness. And even though a lyric poem is usually serious, it can also be funny.

WHAT ARE THE SPECIAL TEXT FEATURES OF POETRY?

The features of a poem look a lot different on the page than a story does. Here are some things to look for in a poem.

Lines

A poem is broken up into **lines** of different lengths. A line may be a complete sentence or part of a sentence. One sentence may spread over several lines of the poem.

The lines of a poem can also have a regular rhythm pattern. Each line may have the same number of **beats**, or accented syllables. Other poems may have a different rhythm for each line.

Stanzas

A **stanza** is a group of lines in a poem. A stanza may have a regular pattern of beats or rhymes. Some short poems are only made up of one stanza. Longer poems made up of two or more stanzas usually have a space between them.

Rhyme

Rhyme is when two lines of a poem end in the same sound. Rhyming gives a poem a special sound and pattern. Not all poems rhyme, however.

Media Connection

Songs contain lines that form **verses** that are like stanzas. Try singing or humming a song such as "Twinkle, Twinkle, Little Star" or "Row, Row, Row Your Boat." Now try clapping along with each beat. Do you notice that the lines have a rhythm like a song, and that they rhyme?

Listen to the words of a **jingle**, or song that goes with a TV or radio commercial. How does the music make it easy to find the rhythm of the lines? Songs for advertisements are written to be catchy so that they stick in people's minds. They are written to persuade the audience to buy the item that the advertisement and song are about.

Directions   Read the poem. Answer the questions that follow.

The Toaster
—William Jay Smith

A silver-scaled dragon with jaws flaming red
Sits at my elbow and toasts my bread.
I hand him fat slices, and then, one by one,
He hands them back when he sees they are done.

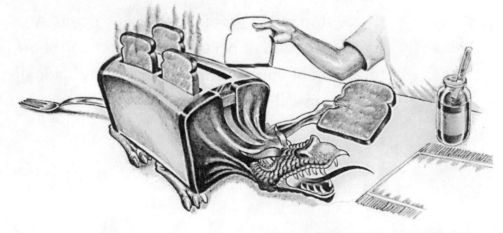

1. How many lines are in this poem?

   _____

2. Circle the rhyming words at the ends of the lines.

3. Who are the two characters in this poem?

   _____

4. What happens to the characters in this poem?

   _____

   _____

   _____

5. What kind of animal is the toaster being compared with?

   _____

6. In most stories, the dragon is usually a scary animal. However,
   the poet shows he is not afraid of the dragon in this poem.
   Underline the details that show he is not frightened.

7. How does the picture fit the message of this poem?

   _____

Understand the
author's purpose
and the
reader's purpose.

WHAT IS THE AUTHOR'S PURPOSE IN WRITING A POEM?

A poet has a purpose in mind when writing a poem. Usually he or she wants to express an important idea about things like life, nature, or art. This idea is the theme of the poem. The theme may not be directly stated in words. As a reader, you may have to figure it out by reading the poem carefully.

WHAT IS THE READER'S PURPOSE WHEN READING A POEM?

When you read a poem, think about your purpose for reading it. It may be one of the following:

- to understand the important idea or message that the poet is presenting
- to enjoy the beauty of the poem in its language and form
- to follow the story of the poem
- to compare details in the poem with details in your own life

To carry out your purpose as a reader, you will need to name **cause and effect**, distinguish **fact** from **opinion**, and identify **main idea** and **supporting details**.

Directions Find a partner and choose a narrative poem that you like. Take turns reading it aloud. List important ideas about the poem. Write these ideas in the chart below.

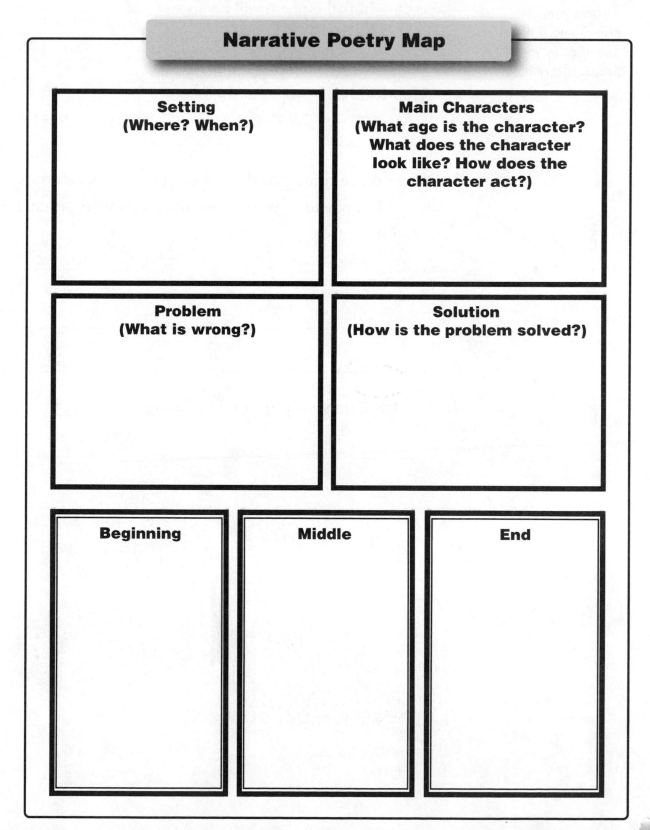

Narrative Poetry Map

Setting
(Where? When?)

Main Characters
(What age is the character? What does the character look like? How does the character act?)

Problem
(What is wrong?)

Solution
(How is the problem solved?)

Beginning

Middle

End

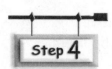

Step 4

Put your prereading skills together as you prepare to read.

Directions Answer the following questions.

1. You will read a poem called "Since Hanna Moved Away." Who do you think the poem will be about?

    _____

2. What will be the topic of the poem?

    _____

3. How do you think people feel when their friends move away? If a friend of yours ever moved away, describe how you felt.

    _____

    _____

    _____

4. What will be your purpose in reading this poem?

    _____

Step 1

Read and/or listen to whole texts.

You are about to read a poem and answer questions about it. Write your answers on the Lyric Poetry Map on the next page. The questions will help you to:

- decide on the purpose of the poem
- name causes and effects, distinguish facts from opinions, and identify main ideas and supporting details
- find the poem's theme
- use pictures to understand the poem's theme
- use questions to examine the poem
- follow the main comparison in the poem
- make decisions about the way the poem is written
- summarize the poem
- create your own ideas about the poem's theme
- read independently

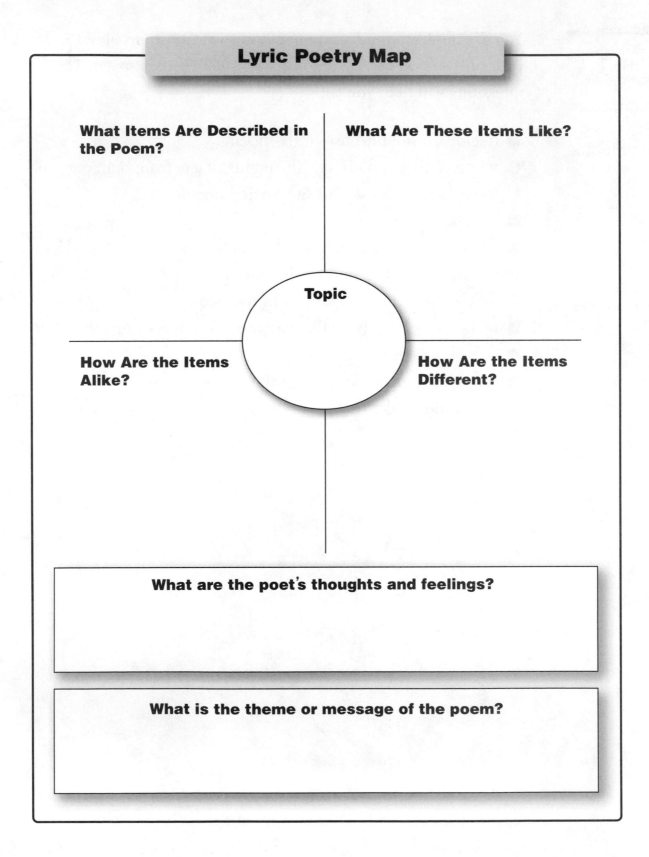

Lyric Poetry Map

What Items Are Described in the Poem?

What Are These Items Like?

Topic

How Are the Items Alike?

How Are the Items Different?

What are the poet's thoughts and feelings?

What is the theme or message of the poem?

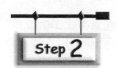

Step 2

Study important words from the story.

You will need to know the following words for the poem. Read the words and think about their meaning. Look for the words as you read the poem. Think about how the words are used in the poem.

prunes	plums dried in the same way as raisins
grouchy	in a bad mood; grumpy

Step 3

Use word skills to increase your vocabulary.

WHAT ARE SOME TOOLS FOR LEARNING NEW WORDS?

As you read and listen, you will learn new words. Every new word you learn will help increase your **vocabulary**. As a reader, there are some helpful questions you can ask yourself to learn new words.

Decide how to say the word.

- What sound does each **vowel** and **consonant** stand for?
- When pronounced together, do the vowels and consonants sound like a word you have heard before?
- Can the word be pronounced in more than one way?

Find the parts that make up a compound word.

- What **syllables** make up the word?
- Does the word have a **prefix** or a **suffix**?
- What is the **root**?

Decide how the word fits in its context.

- What is the poem about?
- What point is the writer making in the poem?
- How does the word's line add to the meaning of the poem?

Directions Read each paragraph below. Say the underlined word aloud. Study the meaning of each sentence. Write a definition for the word. Use a dictionary or glossary to check your work.

1. A <u>pesky</u> pet is like a bug
   Whose buzzing will not end.
   You wish that it would go away
   Until you need a friend.

   _____

   _____

2. Scrape, scrape, scratch, and roll
   Hum the wheels on which you skate.
   The wind then whispers <u>melodies</u>
   That you have never sung.

   _____

Step 4

Understand imagery found in some forms of poetry.

WHAT IS IMAGERY?

Figurative language is words and ideas that are used imaginatively. The meaning goes beyond the words' definitions to create pictures, or images, in the readers' minds. Poets use figurative language to create this **imagery**. Readers enjoy imagery when they use their imagination and other senses to learn about a poet's thoughts and feelings. Identifying these ideas also helps readers learn a poet's purpose and theme.

Three kinds of figurative language used in many poems are **simile, metaphor,** and **personification**. The chart on the next page will help you learn about the similarities and differences of these forms.

Figurative Language

What is figurative language?	What are some examples?	How do readers identify figurative language?
A **simile** uses the words *like* or *as* to compare two different things.	The willow branches moved as gracefully as dancers.	Do you usually compare branches of a tree with human dancers? Of course not. But when you let your imagination see willow branches as dancers, you also understand how graceful the branches looked to the poet.
A **metaphor** compares different things without using the words *like* or *as*.	My song is the ocean's roar and the wind's whistle.	Can a person sing the sounds made by the ocean or the wind? Of course he or she can't. When you let your imagination hear this kind of voice, you have imagined the way that the poet heard these sounds.
Personification is when something that is not human is made to seem like a human.	The moon sang to its parent, the sun.	Can the moon sing? Is the sun a parent to the moon? These are human qualities. They are used to express the poet's feelings about the sun and the moon.

READING WITH COMPREHENSION

Reading Guide	Guided Questions

Step 5

Understand poetry by examining word choice and literary elements.

Directions Put it all together now. Use all the strategies you have learned so far. They will help you read "Since Hanna Moved Away." Look at the questions and comments on the right-hand side, They will help improve your comprehension of this example of poetry.

①
Since Hanna Moved Away
—Judith Viorst

The tires on my bike are flat.

② The sky is grouchy gray.

At least it sure feels like that

③ Since Hanna moved away.

④ Chocolate ice cream tastes like prunes.
December's come to stay,
They've taken back the Mays and Junes
Since Hanna moved away.

Nothing's fun to laugh about,
Nothing's fun to play.

⑤ They call me, but I won't come out

⑥ Since Hanna moved away.

① What must have happened before this poem was written?

② The sky is a certain color of gray. Circle the word that tells what this color is like. Is this an example of simile, metaphor, or personification? How can you tell?

③ How does the poet feel since Hanna moved away?

④ What has happened to the poet's taste of food?

⑤ What do the people want the poet to do?

⑥ Why does the poet have these feelings?

Directions Use details from the poem to answer the following questions. Fill in the circle beside the answer that you choose.

1. What mood is the poet in since Hanna moved away?

Ⓐ happy

Ⓑ mean

Ⓒ unhappy

Ⓓ silly

2. What two things are compared in the simile that begins the second stanza?

Ⓐ December is compared with Hanna.

Ⓑ Chocolate is compared with ice cream.

Ⓒ Ice cream is compared with December.

Ⓓ Chocolate ice cream is compared with prunes.

3. What does the poet mean when she says, "December's come to stay"?

Ⓐ It feels like winter and bad weather all the time.

Ⓑ She is looking forward to starting a new year.

Ⓒ It is sad since Hanna won't be around for her birthday.

Ⓓ Everything is as exciting as Christmas and Hannukah.

4. What is the theme, or message, of this poem?

Ⓐ People care very deeply for everyday things.

Ⓑ It's no fun when a good friend moves away.

Ⓒ It is usually too hard to keep in touch when friends move away.

Ⓓ Feelings affect all of the senses, but especially taste and touch.

5. **What is another good title for this poem?**

(A) Summer Days

(B) New Homes

(C) It's Winter All the Time

(D) Why I Love to Stay Inside

For the open-ended questions, remember to:
- **Focus your response on the question asked.**
- **Answer all parts of the question.**
- **Give a complete explanation.**
- **Use specific information from the directions.**

---

6. **Which of the five senses do you use to understand the second stanza?**

- Explain the things compared in the simile.

- Describe the kind of weather that the poet talks about.

Use details from the selection to support your answer.

_____

_____

_____

_____

_____

_____

7. Who are the people the poet is talking about in the last stanza when she says, "They call me, but I won't come out . . ."?

- Describe the different people who are still living in the poet's community.

- List the kinds of activities that most children have to do during the day.

- Explain why the people would want the poet to come out.

Use details from the selection to support your answer.

_____

_____

_____

_____

_____

_____

NJ ASK Practice

Directions Following this set of directions are multiple-choice and open-ended questions. Fill in the circle beside the answer that you choose for questions 1 through 5. Write answers to questions 6 and 7.

Bottle Penguin
by Debbie Anilonis

What you need:

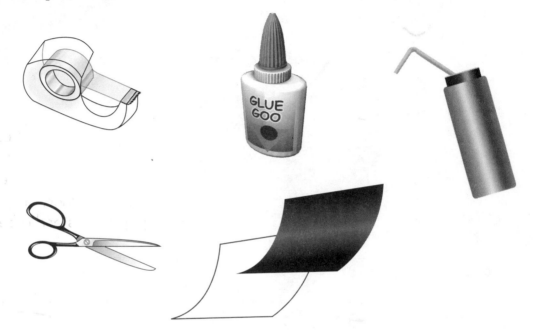

How to make it:

1. To make the body, tape black paper around a clean plastic bottle. Cut out an oval shape from white paper, and glue it to the front of the body.

2. To make a scarf, cut out a long strip of paper and glue it around the top of the body. Then cut out two paper scarf ends, and glue them on.

3. Cut out wings from black paper, and glue them to the back of the body.

4. To make the head, cut out a black circle and a smaller white circle from paper. Glue the white circle onto the black, then glue on cut-paper eyes and a beak.

5. Cut out a hat from paper, and glue it on the head. Glue the head to the front of the bottle cap.

6. Cut out two paper feet, and glue them to the bottom of the bottle.

1. **What will be turned into a penguin?**

   Ⓐ scissors

   Ⓑ bottle

   Ⓒ tape

   Ⓓ feathers

2. **Which of the following is NOT something you need to complete this project?**

   Ⓐ glue

   Ⓑ paper

   Ⓒ pencil

   Ⓓ scissors

3. **What part of the penguin is made first?**

   Ⓐ the eyes

   Ⓑ the wings

   Ⓒ the head

   Ⓓ the body

4. **Why is the head made before the eyes?**

   Ⓐ so that the eyes can be glued onto the head

   Ⓑ because the eyes are smaller than the head

   Ⓒ so that the eyes will be the same shape as the head

   Ⓓ because the eyes must first be glued onto the beak

5. **What are the last three tools used to complete the bottle penguin?**

   Ⓐ paper, tape, and the bottle cap

   Ⓑ paper, scissors, and glue

   Ⓒ tape, glue, and scissors

   Ⓓ the bottle cap, paper, and glue

For the open-ended questions, remember to:
- Focus your response on the question asked.
- Answer all parts of the question.
- Give a complete explanation.
- Use specific information from the directions.

6. Why is it important to follow the steps in the order they are written? Summarize each step. Descibe how the parts of the penguin are made. Explain how you know where to place each part on the penguin.

   Use details from the selection to support your answer.

   _____

   _____

   _____

   _____

   _____

7. What kind of story might have a character like
   this penguin? Describe the weather at the South Pole
   where penguins live. Explain the kind of story in which
   a penguin would wear a hat and scarf. List an event
   that might happen in the story.

   Use details from the selection to support your answer.

   _____

   _____

   _____

   _____

   _____

   _____

Focus on the New Jersey CCCS

Have you ever written a letter or a postcard? How did you know what to write? Did someone help you write it? To whom did you write it? How does writing every day help you?

Guided Instruction

Directions Look at the picture below. Then answer the questions. Use crayons, colored markers, or colored pens to follow the directions.

1. What are the pupils doing?

_____

2. Who is reading a recipe? Color this person's shirt red.

_____

3. Who is reading the label of a can? Color this person's shirt green.

_____

_____

Focus on the New Jersey CCCS

Authors have many different reasons, or purposes, for writing. Did an author write a story to make readers laugh? Was it written to explain something? Was it written to give ideas about something? Was it written to give information?

Guided Instruction

It is important to think about your **purpose** when you write. Just like an author, your purpose is your **reason** for writing. You might want to entertain your readers. You might want to persuade your readers to feel the same way you do about a subject. Or, you might want to **inform** your readers with facts about a topic.

PARK RULES:
1. No running on sidewalk
2. Balls and bats on field ONLY
3. No jumping off swings
4. Take turns on the climbing toy

Have you ever been to a park in your community and noticed a sign with a list of rules? Why are safety rules important to read and follow? Imagine that you have been asked to write a list that will teach safety rules to your classmates. These safety rules will be used for your school playground. There should be five rules. Each rule needs to be explained in one sentence. The list will be posted on all of the school bulletin boards. What will be your purpose for this piece of writing?

Directions Use the prewriting steps below to help you decide and organize.

Decide on the topic of your writing and your audience.

Decide on your purpose, or why you are writing.

Decide how to meet your purpose for writing.

1. What will you be writing about?

   I will be writing the rules for the playground.

2. Who will be reading what you write?

   Kids who go to the playground

3. Why are you writing this list?

   I am writing this list to make sure noone gets hurt.

4. What will be your purpose for writing this list?

   I will write this list for kids so they don't hurt themselves.

5. Will you make your rules funny and entertaining? Why or why not?

   I will not make my rules funny and entertaining. because we need to make sure know one gets hurt.

6. Will your rules tell a story? Why or why not?

   No they will not tell a story because I need to teach kids how to be safe

7. What would be the best way to tell your readers about playground rules?

   The best way to tell my readers about playground rules is write n sighn be kind.

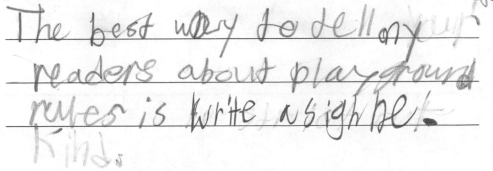

Ideas to Remember

purpose—the reason for doing something
inform—give readers facts about something

Apply the New Jersey CPIs

Directions Graphic organizers are designed to help you with organization. There are many different kinds of graphic organizers. A good one to use when you are just starting to write is called an Idea Web, or Description Web. Look at the Idea Web below. Use this Idea Web to brainstorm some safety rules.

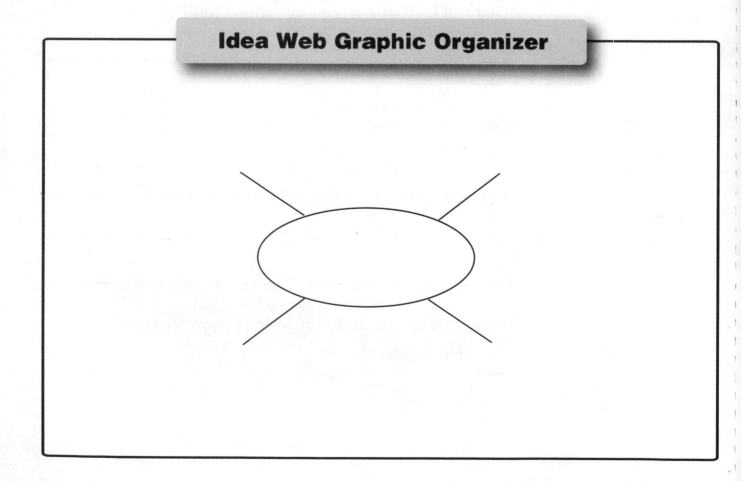

Idea Web Graphic Organizer

To start, put the subject of your informational piece in the center oval. Draw ovals at the ends of the lines coming out from the center. Use these ovals to write in your ideas, details, and facts as you think of them. Not every idea or fact will come to you, but creating this organizer will give you a head start. If you need more space, draw more lines and ovals.

Directions When you have finished writing the facts and details, use them to write some sample sentences on the lines below.

_____

_____

_____

_____

_____

_____

_____

_____

_____

Writing to Inform—List

Use the ideas you came up with in the Idea Web to create your list of five safety rules. Each rule must be a full sentence. Include anwers to some of the following questions in your list.

- What are some important safety rules?
- Why should students follow these rules?
- Have any problems happened on the playground that need specific safety rules?

Use your own paper or write in your literary response journal.

Here is a checklist for you to follow to help you do your best writing. Before you begin writing, read the checklist silently. Reread it as often as you need to.

Writer's Checklist

Remember to:

❑ Keep the central idea or topic in mind.

❑ Keep your audience in mind.

❑ Support your ideas with details, explanations, and examples.

❑ State your ideas in a clear sequence.

❑ Include an opening and a closing.

❑ Use a variety of words and vary your sentence structure.

❑ State your opinion or conclusion clearly.

❑ Capitalize, spell, and use punctuation correctly.

❑ Write neatly.

After you write your list, read what you have written. Use the checklist to make certain that your writing is the best it can be. Begin to collect your writing to keep in a folder. As you write, look back and compare your new writing with what you have done before.

Focus on the New Jersey CCCS

When you describe something, what is your purpose? When you are telling about an event, or something that happened, why do you tell it like a story?

Guided Instruction

Sometimes authors will **write to describe** an event or an experience to readers. In this case, their purpose would be to share what they saw with readers. Another purpose would be to **entertain** readers. You can write to **narrate,** or tell about something you did. Just like an author, your purpose would be to share an experience with your readers or to entertain them.

Think about a hobby that you are very good at, and imagine that you were in a contest for it this past weekend. You will write a story telling your readers about it. Decide what your purpose would be for writing this story. Then think about how you would share your information with your readers.

Directions   Read the steps and answer the questions.

Step 1

Decide on the topic of your writing and your audience.

1. What will you be writing about?

    _____

2. Who will be reading what you write?

    _____

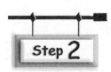

Step 2

Decide why you are writing, or your purpose for writing.

3. Why are you writing this narrative?

    _____

4. What will be your purpose for writing this narrative?

    _____

    _____

Step 3

Decide how to meet your purpose for writing.

5. Will you make your story funny and entertaining? Why or why not?

_____

_____

_____

6. Will your narrative tell a story? Why or why not?

_____

_____

7. What would you say to introduce your readers to your narrative?

_____

_____

 Ideas to Remember

describe—to share what something looked or sounded like with an audience

narrate—to tell a story to an audience

Apply the New Jersey CPIs

Directions Suppose that you are writing a paragraph to tell friends about shopping for new school clothes. Read the following sentences. Find the sentences that would go into your paragraph. Cross out the sentences that would not go into the paragraph. On the lines below, write the sentences that you would use. Put them in order. Then write your paragraph on a separate sheet of paper.

- Have you ever been in a pet store?
- I tried on ten pairs of shoes.
- Yesterday I went shopping for new school clothes.
- I wanted black jeans.
- I need help with my math.
- We finally found a pair that I liked.
- Then we looked for new jeans.
- After a while, we agreed that I could get one black pair.
- I'm going to make play clay with my brother.
- My mom wanted me to get dark blue.
- The others had to be dark blue.
- I don't like shopping for clothes.

6) I tried on ten pairs of shoes

1) Yesterday I went shopping for new
school clothein g

2) I wanted black jeans

4) We finally found a pair that
we liked

3) Then we looked for new jeans

7) After a while, we agreed that I
could get one black pair

5) my mom wanted me to get
dark blue!

5) The others had to be dark blue.

Writing to Describe

Write a paragraph to describe your favorite animal. This can be any animal. If you own a pet, you can describe it. Think about the following things as you plan your writing. Use words that make your meaning clear.

- What kind of animal are you describing?
- What does the animal eat?
- What does the animal look like?
- Where does this animal live?

You may take notes, create a web, or do other prewriting work. Then write your description. Use your own paper or write in your literary response journal.

Here is a checklist for you to follow to help you do your best writing. Before you begin writing, read the checklist silently. Reread it as often as you need.

Writer's Checklist

Remember to:

❑ Keep the central idea or topic in mind.

❑ Keep your audience in mind.

❑ Support your ideas with details, explanations, and examples.

❑ State your ideas in a clear sequence.

❑ Include an opening and a closing.

❑ Use a variety of words and vary your sentence structure.

❑ State your opinion or conclusion clearly.

❑ Capitalize, spell, and use punctuation correctly.

❑ Write neatly.

After you write your composition, read what you have written. Use the checklist to make certain that your writing is the best it can be. Begin to collect your writing to keep in a folder. As you write, look back and compare your new writing with what you have done before.

Focus on the New Jersey CCCS

Have you ever tried to describe something you really liked? Have you ever tried to get a friend to agree with you? How do TV ads try to get you to buy something?

Guided Instruction

All writing has a purpose, or a reason. One purpose for writing is to **persuade** people to agree with the writer's ideas. For example, writers persuade us to buy a new CD or game. **Persuasive** writing is written to persuade someone to think or act a certain way.

Persuasive writers often say things that make you want to agree with them. If a writer wants you to buy something, he or she may write, "This is 30% better than the leading brand." People who read or see this information may buy it because it sounds good.

Directions Look at the graphic organizer. Read each detail. Think about the way the writer states these ideas. Then follow the steps.

Organize Writing to Persuade

Opening Sentence

Our neighborhood is planning a clean-up day for the park.

Main Idea

Next Saturday, some of our neighbors plan to clean up the trash in the park.

Details	**Examples**
No one can enjoy the park until it is cleaned up.	No one has used the park for fun for several months.
Bushes and trees need trimming.	Trees and bushes have several dead limbs.
Flower beds are full of weeds.	Flowers are dying because they are not cared for. Water in the stream is not clean. The stream bed is ugly.
The stream is full of trash.	
The ground is covered with litter.	People have thrown their trash all over the ground.

Closing Sentence

Please help us clean up our park so that everyone can enjoy it again.

Write an opening that tells your purpose for writing.

1. What event does this writer want readers to know about?

_____

_____

Tell the main idea you want to present about your topic.

2. What point will all the details support?

_____

_____

List details for each paragraph you will write.

3. How does the writer support the main idea?

_____

_____

4. Why does the writer list examples for each detail?

_____

_____

_____

Write a closing that sums up what you want to say or tells how you feel about your topic.

5. What does the closing ask readers to do?

_____

_____

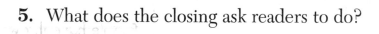

(Ideas to Remember)

persuade—to convince readers to agree with the writer's ideas

Apply the New Jersey CPIs

Directions Imagine you are planning to write a persuasive letter to your town's mayor to convince him or her to start an after-school recreation center in your town. Use the list of details below to help you complete the Sequencing List. This graphic organizer is designed to help you put sentences in an order that makes sense. Remember to put your ideas and details into sentences.

- Many kids need a place to go after school.
- Most parents in your community are at work.
- There is no place in your community for kids to play after school.
- Volunteers could help with homework.
- Kids need a place to play together.

Sequencing List

Opening Sentence
Main Idea
Detail
Detail
Detail
Closing

Writing to Persuade—Letter

**NJ ASK
Practice**

Imagine that many of the kids in your town have nowhere to go after school. Just like you, their parents work. After discussing the problem with your family, they suggest you write a persuasive letter to the mayor about starting an after-school recreation center in your town. You think it is an important idea that everyone can benefit from. Using the information in the Sequencing List you just completed, and your own ideas, try to write a letter persuading the mayor to open an after-school recreation program.

Use your own paper or write in your literary response journal.

Here is a checklist for you to follow to help you do your best writing. Before you begin writing, read the checklist silently. Reread it as often as you need.

Writer's Checklist

Remember to:

❒ Keep the central idea or topic in mind.

❒ Keep your audience in mind.

❒ Support your ideas with details, explanations, and examples.

❒ State your ideas in a clear sequence.

❒ Include an opening and a closing.

❒ Use a variety of words and vary your sentence structure.

❒ State your opinion or conclusion clearly.

❒ Capitalize, spell, and use punctuation correctly.

❒ Write neatly.

After you write your composition, read what you have written. Use the checklist to make certain that your writing is the best it can be.

Focus on the New Jersey CCCS

Do you have friends who always make you feel happy? Do you know someone who always makes you feel sad or angry? How can writing affect you the same way?

Guided Instruction

Every writer has a different way of writing. Some writers write only mystery stories. Others may write only things that are funny. One writer might use long sentences with hard words. Another writer might write in short sentences and use easy words. The way a writer writes is called the **writer's style,** or **voice.** The writer's style and voice can affect the way readers feel about what the writer is trying to say.

Think about your own writing. How would you describe your own voice as a writer? Put a check next to the items that describe your voice as a writer.

_____   My writing is usually funny.

_____   My writing is usually realistic.

_____   My writing is usually fictional.

_____   My writing is usually serious.

_____   My writing is usually informational.

Directions Read along as this story is read to you. Try taking notes on the important points. Think about the writer's voice. Then answer the questions.

Yesterday I helped my Dad paint my room. I don't think he'll let me do that again. He poured the paint into a tray and put the tray on the floor. Then he opened the ladder and set it by the first wall. He climbed up the ladder and asked me to hand him a rag. I picked up the rag and stepped over to the ladder. As I held it up, I heard him say, "Jeff, watch what you're doing."

I looked around and didn't see anything. I put my foot on the floor for balance. I guess I should have looked on the floor because I stepped right into the paint tray. It was a good thing that Dad had put down a cover on the floor. My shoe was squishy with paint. Dad climbed down from the ladder. It took us a long time to clean my shoe.

Back in my room, Dad filled my roller with paint and then handed it to me. A fly flew by my nose, and I swatted at it. *Splat*!

The roller smashed against Dad. He now had paint running down his arm. He left the room to change shirts and wash his arm. When he came back, he took the roller from me and put it back in the tray. "That's all right, Jeff. I can finish this job by myself. I want to make sure we have enough paint left for the walls."

Maybe tomorrow I'll help Mom in the flower garden.

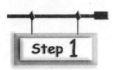

Decide what tone
you will use in
your writing.

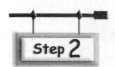

Decide how you will
give your writing the
tone you have chosen.

Set your tone, or
voice at the
beginning of
your writing.

Keep the same
voice through
the whole story.

1. Is this story funny, sad, or serious?

I think this story is funny

2. How does the writer make this story funny?

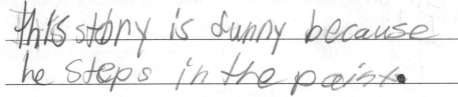

this story is funny because
he steps in the paint.

3. What does the writer say at the beginning that sets the tone
for this story?

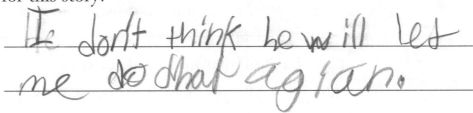

I don't think he will let
me do that agian.

4. What funny scene does the writer describe first?

he steps in paint

5. What is the next funny scene that he describes?

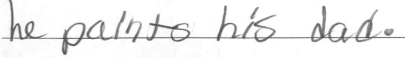

he paints his dad.

6. What does he say at the end that could lead to another
funny story?

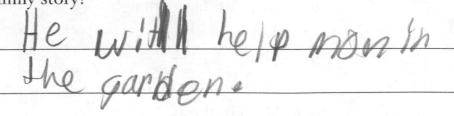

He will help mom in
the garden.

Yesterday I went shopping for new
school clothing. I tried on ten pairs
of shoes. We finally found a pair that
I liked. Then we looked for new jeans.
I wanted black jeans. My mom
wanted me to get the dark blue
blue. After awile, we agreed
that I could get one black pair.
The others had to be dark blue.

① coppy ②

① Yesterday I went shopping for new school clothes. I wanted black jeans. The others had to be dark blue. ③ We finally found a pair that I liked. Then we looked for more jeans. My mom wanted me to get the dark blue ones. After a wile we agreed that I could get one black pair. ② I tried ten pairs of shoes.

Ideas to Remember

> **writer's voice**—the way a writer writes
>
> **tone**—the feeling of a piece of writing; it might be scary, funny, sad, or serious

Apply the New Jersey CPIs

Directions Suppose you are planning to write a one-paragraph story about something funny that happened to you or someone you know. Answer the following questions to form a writing plan. Fill out the Sequencing List on the next page.

1. What voice will you use in your paragraph?

   _____

2. What funny thing will you write about?

   _____

3. Write two or three sentences on the chart with details that made this event funny.

4. How will you show your voice at the beginning of your paragraph? Write your opening sentence on the chart.

5. Write a closing sentence on the chart to show your voice.

Sequencing List

Opening Sentence

Main Idea

Detail

Detail

Detail

Closing

Writing to Entertain—Letter

Imagine you have been asked to write a funny article for your town's newspaper. The editor doesn't care what it's about, as long as it's funny and at least three paragraphs long. The purpose of your article should be to entertain your audience. Using the information you wrote for the Sequencing List, try to expand your letter into three paragraphs.

Write your article using your own paper or write in your literary response journal.

Here is a checklist for you to follow to help you do your best writing. Before you begin writing, read the checklist silently. Reread it as often as you need.

Writer's Checklist

Remember to:

❐ Keep the central idea or topic in mind.

❐ Keep your audience in mind.

❐ Support your ideas with details, explanations, and examples.

❐ State your ideas in a clear sequence.

❐ Include an opening and a closing.

❐ Use a variety of words and vary your sentence structure.

❐ State your opinion or conclusion clearly.

❐ Capitalize, spell, and use punctuation correctly.

❐ Write neatly.

After you write your article, read what you have written. Use the checklist to make certain that your writing is the best it can be.

Focus on the New Jersey CCCS

How do teams win games? They often have a **strategy**, or a **plan.** What kinds of games do you play that need a strategy to win?

Guided Instruction

A **writing strategy** is a plan designed to help you write. There are different kinds of writing strategies. Some writing strategies you might use are listed below.

- **Brainstorming**—Write down all the ideas you can think of about one topic. When you are done, check over your list. Try to find ideas that go together. Decide which ideas are best. Choose the ones that best fit your writing task. Graphic organizers are good brainstorming tools. Some of these are a Word or Idea Web, a list, and a chart.

- **Discussion**—Talk about a topic with other pupils. Listen carefully to their ideas. Are their ideas like yours? Take notes on the ideas that interest you most.

- **KWL**—Make a chart. This chart will lead you to find information that you can use in your writing. List what you already **know** about your topic. Next, list what you **want** to learn about the topic. Then, list what you have **learned** about the topic. Look at this sample KWL chart.

What I **K**now	What I **W**ant to Learn	What I **L**earned

● **Role-playing**—Act out a story as a skit, or short play. Work with other pupils. What happens when two pupils can't agree? Later, talk about your skit. List ideas about what happened. Which ones will help you write your own story?

● **Journal-writing**—Keep a record of your ideas in a journal. List things that interest you. List interesting things that happen to you. Tell how you feel about these things.

● **Drawing**—Record an idea with a picture. Suppose you must write about an animal. Choose one animal and draw its picture. Next, make a list of ideas about the animal in your picture. Use these ideas to write about this animal. You might also draw characters in a story. List ideas about each character. Use these details as you write the story.

Directions You want to write about your favorite toy. Follow the steps and answer the questions.

Set your topic.

1. What will be your topic?

   _____

2. What do you know about your topic?

   _____

   _____

   _____

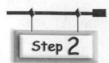

Step 2

Think of
different ideas
about your
topic. List as
many as
you can.

3. What is brainstorming?

_____

_____

4. Brainstorm ideas about your topic. Use a Word Web like the web below. Write your topic in the center oval. Use ideas you listed in question 2. Write them in the other ovals.

Word Web

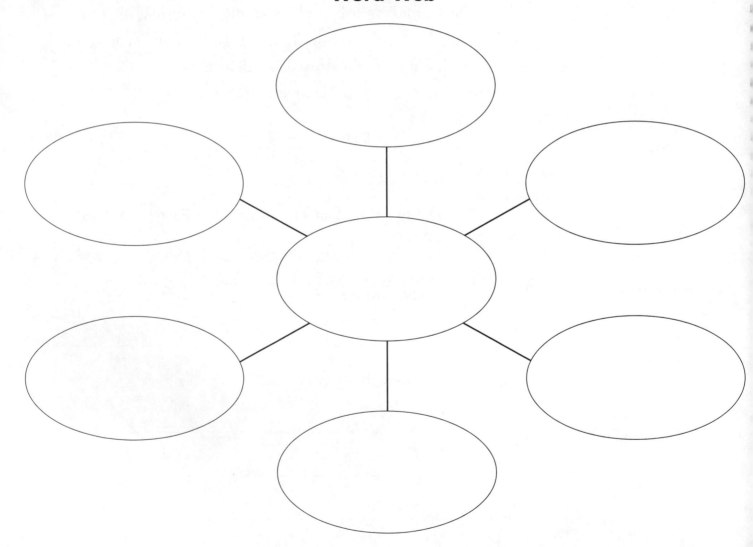

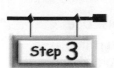

Look for ideas that go together.

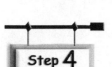

Choose your best ideas for your writing.

5. Think about the ideas in your Word Web. Draw lines to join ideas that go together.

6. Look over the Word Web. Choose the best ideas. Place a check mark beside each one you choose.

7. Why are these good ideas for your topic?

_____

_____

writing strategy—a plan to help you write

brainstorming—writing down as many ideas as you can about a topic

KWL—a chart for what you know about a topic, what you want to learn about a topic, and what you learn about a topic

Apply the New Jersey CPIs

Directions Think about what you know about thunderstorms. Use the KWL chart below. A few facts have been included for you. Find other facts about thunderstorms in an encyclopedia or a library book on tornadoes. List these ideas in the KWL chart.

Topic: Tornadoes

What I **K**now	What I **W**ant to Learn	What I **L**earned
A thunderstorm has loud thunder.	8._____	12._____
	_____	_____
A thunderstorm has lightning.	9._____	13._____
	_____	_____
	10._____	14._____
	_____	_____
Lightning can hurt people and animals.	11._____	15._____
	_____	_____

16. Think about the facts in the chart. Which ones would your readers find most interesting? Put a check by each idea you choose.

 Measuring Up® to the NJ Core Curriculum Content Standards

Writing to Inform—Story

NJ ASK Practice

A thunderstorm can cause damage to an area with the wind, rain, and lightning. Imagine that a thunderstorm is coming toward your area. What will you do? Write a short story about it. Use the KWL Chart to help you with the details.

- **How do you find out a thunderstorm is coming?**
- **Where will you and your family go?**
- **What happens when the thunderstorm comes near you?**
- **What sounds do you hear when the thunderstorm is nearby?**
- **What do you see when the thunderstorm is nearby?**
- **How do you feel when the thunderstorm is nearby?**
- **What happens when the thunderstorm has gone?**

Here is a checklist for you to follow to help you do your best writing. Before you begin writing, read the checklist silently. Reread it as often as you need.

Writer's Checklist

Remember to:

☐ Keep the central idea or topic in mind.

☐ Keep your audience in mind.

☐ Support your ideas with details, explanations, and examples.

☐ State your ideas in a clear sequence.

☐ Include an opening and a closing.

☐ Use a variety of words and vary your sentence structure.

☐ State your opinion or conclusion clearly.

☐ Capitalize, spell, and use punctuation correctly.

☐ Write neatly.

After you write your story, read what you have written. Use the checklist to make certain that your writing is the best it can be.

Focus on the New Jersey CCCS

Do writers always write about only what they know? How do they find information they may need to use? Where are some good places for writers to do research?

Guided Instruction

Eventually, all writers will have to write about topics they know very little about. When writers do not know everything about a topic, they must **research,** or find information. They will often look in libraries for the information they need. To help people find information, libraries have **catalogs,** or **lists,** of the books and magazines they have and the information each one contains.

Most libraries today have their catalogs on computers. If you know what topic you need to research, you can type it into the computer and ask for a search. Librarians can help you. The computer can then show you all the books in the library written about that topic. If you know only the name of the author that you need, you can type the author's name into the computer. The computer will show you the names of all the books in the library written by that author and where you can find them on the shelves.

Look at the examples on the next page.

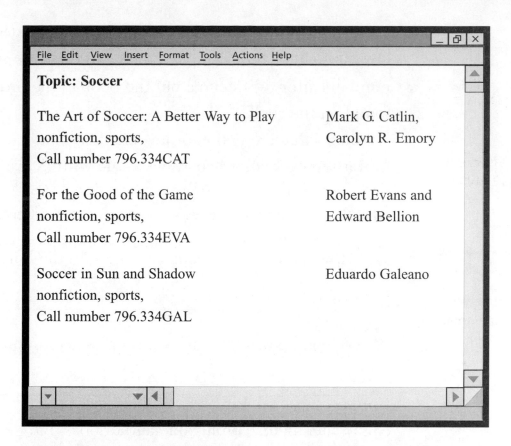

File   Edit   View   Insert   Format   Tools   Actions   Help

Topic: Soccer

The Art of Soccer: A Better Way to Play   Mark G. Catlin,
nonfiction, sports,   Carolyn R. Emory
Call number 796.334CAT

For the Good of the Game   Robert Evans and
nonfiction, sports,   Edward Bellion
Call number 796.334EVA

Soccer in Sun and Shadow   Eduardo Galeano
nonfiction, sports,
Call number 796.334GAL

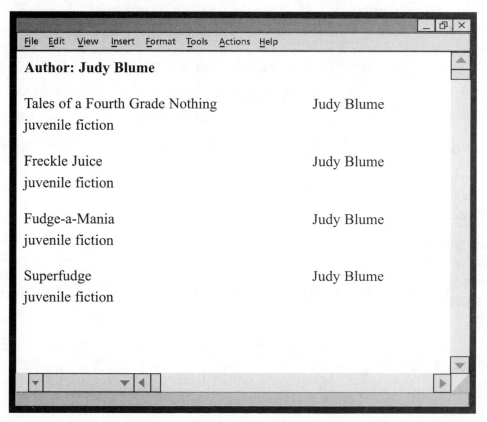

File   Edit   View   Insert   Format   Tools   Actions   Help

Author: Judy Blume

Tales of a Fourth Grade Nothing   Judy Blume
juvenile fiction

Freckle Juice   Judy Blume
juvenile fiction

Fudge-a-Mania   Judy Blume
juvenile fiction

Superfudge   Judy Blume
juvenile fiction

The **call number** of a nonfiction book tells where it is on the library shelf. In the examples, 796 would represent sports. The numbers after the decimal put the book in the order it would be found on the shelf.

Books that are fiction or juvenile fiction are arranged in **alphabetical order**, according to the writer's last name.

Directions   Follow the steps. Then answer the questions.

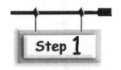

Find books about your topic.

1. How many books about soccer are in the library?

   _____

2. Which book might give steps on how to improve your play?

   _____

3. Which book has only one author?

   _____

4. In which section of the library are all the books on soccer found?

   _____

Decide how you will give your writing the tone you have chosen.

5. Which author wrote all the books listed in the second example?

   _____

6. In which section of the library are all these books found?

   _____

7. Would you find the books under J or B?

   _____

Ideas to Remember

> **library catalog**—a list of the titles and authors of all the books in the library

Apply the New Jersey CPIs

Directions Read the list of books below. Then, answer the questions.

Salty and the Pirates by Marie Delaney

Little House on the Prairie by Laura Ingalls Wilder

The Remarkable Rainforest by Toni Albert, Ada Hanlon

Ed Emberley's Drawing Book of Animals by Ed Emberley

Who Let the Dogs Out? by H.B. Homzie

A Picture Book of Jackie Robinson by David A. Adler, Robert Casilla

Ed Emberley's Drawing Book of Faces by Ed Emberley

Henry and Mudge First Book by Cynthia Rylant

The Everything Kids' Baseball Book by Richard Mintzer

8. Which books would be listed under the topic **Sports?**

   _____

   _____

9. Which books would be listed under the topic **Art?**

   _____

   _____

10. Who wrote *Little House on the Prairie*?

    _____

11. List two books that could be found in the section
    Juvenile Fiction.

    _____

    _____

    _____

12. Which book would be listed under the topic **Science?**

    _____

13. Who is the author of *Henry and Mudge First Book*?

    _____

**NJ ASK
Practice**

Research for Writing

Take a trip to the school or public library. Choose a topic that you would like to research. Find three books that are related to this topic. Write the name of the book, the author, and three sentences that describe what each book is about on a separate sheet of paper.

After you write your list, read what you have written. Go over your list carefully to make certain that your writing is the best it can be.

Focus on the New Jersey CCCS

How do writers remember what they have read or heard? Do they go back to their sources often to ask questions or reread?

Guided Instruction

It is almost impossible for anyone to remember everything that they read or hear. When writers gather information to include in their writing, they **take notes**. There are some very important things to know about taking notes when researching. Some of these are listed below.

Use only the most important details

Learning how to take notes properly is an important step when doing research. Try to write only the **main idea** of each paragraph and the most important details about it. It is unnecessary to include unimportant details that will not help you. For instance, if you are writing about Abraham Lincoln's Gettysburg Address, it is not necessary to know that he sometimes wore a stovepipe hat. But it is important to know the reason why he was giving the speech.

Your notes do not have to be complete sentences

Taking notes should be a quick exercise. It should not be something that takes long to do or distracts you from your research. Try writing only **key words** and ideas. Full sentences can be written later. However, if you are using **direct quotes** from an interview or written document, it is very important to be sure you have quoted these words correctly. For example, if you want to include exact words from the Gettysburg Address to make a point, be sure to put quotes around those words like this, **"Four score and seven years ago..."**

Remember where you found the notes

Sometimes you will be asked to provide a **bibliography,** or a list of the sources and books where you found all the facts. Try to write page numbers and book titles next to your notes to help you later. Lincoln made the speech at the dedication of a war cemetery—pg 25, <u>Lincoln's Gettysburg Address</u>

Reread your notes later

When the research is finished and it comes time to write the report, going back to the notes and **rereading** them is not only helpful, but it is important to do. Rereading will help you remember exactly what it is you read and why it is important.

Directions Read this paragraph that a student wrote after doing research. Then follow the steps and answer the questions.

Cats are now more popular as pets than dogs are. More people own cats than dogs. In the past, the opposite was true. More people owned dogs. The change may have happened because so many people live in apartments today. Cats get exercise by climbing and playing. However, dogs need to run and play. There are no yards in apartments for them to run in. Cats curl up and sleep a lot, even when they are young. Most dogs sleep little during the day, so they look for things to entertain them. If their owners aren't home, they might tear up pillows and other things just to keep busy. Cats can use litter boxes and can take care of themselves. Dogs must be walked every morning and night. They need the help of people. Perhaps today people are so busy that they like pets that can take care of themselves.

Directions   Listen as your teacher models this activity. Follow the steps.
Answer the questions. Reread the paragraph to find information, if you need to.

Step 1

Find the main idea.

Step 2

Include
important
details.

Step 3

Include
examples.

1. What is the main idea of this paragraph?

    _____

2. What is one reason the writer thinks more people choose
    cats as pets?

    _____

3. What is another reason the writer thinks more people choose
    cats as pets?

    _____

    _____

4. What is one reason the writer thinks cats are better to have
    in apartments?

    _____

    _____

5. What is another reason why cats are better to have
    in apartments?

    _____

    _____

6. What is a third reason why cats are better to have
    in apartments?

    _____

    _____

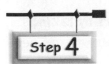

Step 4

Organize your notes.

7. You can use this Concept Map to arrange your notes.

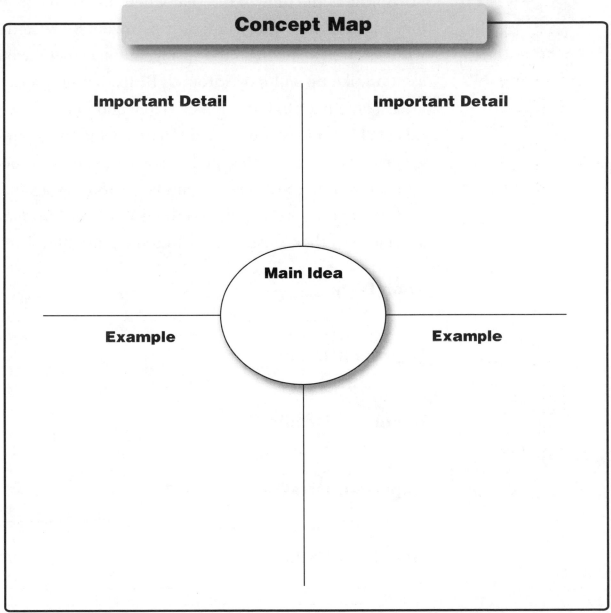

Concept Map

Important Detail

Important Detail

Main Idea

Example

Example

Ideas to Remember

main idea—the main point that a writer makes

detail—a fact that supports or tells about the main idea

example—a fact that tells about a detail or the main idea

Apply the New Jersey CPIs

Directions Read the paragraph below. Then fill out the chart by taking notes in your own words about the paragraph.

Spring is the time of the year when the earth comes back to life. In the winter, everything seems frozen. Snow and ice melt with warmer weather. In the spring, animals that have been asleep wake up and move around. Birds that flew away to warmer areas come back to their homes. They build nests, lay eggs, and raise babies. Flowers that died bloom again. Trees put out new, green leaves. Grass, trees, and other plants that had been covered with snow and ice turn green and begin to grow again. Streams that had been frozen melt, and the water begins to move. Warmer weather causes the earth to be a brighter, livelier place.

Main Idea:

_____

Important Detail:

_____

Important Detail:

_____

Important Detail:

_____

Important Detail:

_____

Important Detail:

_____

_____

Conclusion:

_____

_____

Using Notes

NJ ASK
Practice

Using the notes you took in the chart, rewrite the paragraph in your own words. Be careful. You never want to use the same ideas and words that another writer has already used.

Use your own paper or write in your literary response journal.

Here is a checklist for you to follow to help you do your best writing. Before you begin writing, read the checklist silently. Reread it as often as you need.

Writer's Checklist

Remember to:

- ❏ Keep the central idea or topic in mind.
- ❏ Keep your audience in mind.
- ❏ Support your ideas with details, explanations, and examples.
- ❏ State your ideas in a clear sequence.
- ❏ Include an opening and a closing.
- ❏ Use a variety of words and vary your sentence structure.
- ❏ State your opinion or conclusion clearly.
- ❏ Capitalize, spell, and use punctuation correctly.
- ❏ Write neatly.

After you write your composition, read what you have written. Use the checklist to make certain that your writing is the best it can be.

Focus on the New Jersey CCCS

What is a topic? Why does a piece of writing need a topic? How do writers find topics? Choosing a topic is the first step in writing. Once you have that, then you have to find out what main point you will make.

Guided Instruction

A **topic** is the subject of a piece of writing, or what you will write about. A **Word Web** or an **Idea Web** is a good way to **brainstorm**. It can help you narrow your focus for your writing. Think freely as you brainstorm. Write down every topic that comes to mind.

Look at the web below. Your assignment is to write a report about one of our country's national monuments. Write the words "National Monuments" in the center circle. Brainstorm possible topic ideas about national monuments. It's best to start with general ideas. Write these ideas in the outer circles. When you have finished brainstorming, choose one of these topic ideas to write about. Place a check mark by the topic you chose.

Idea Web

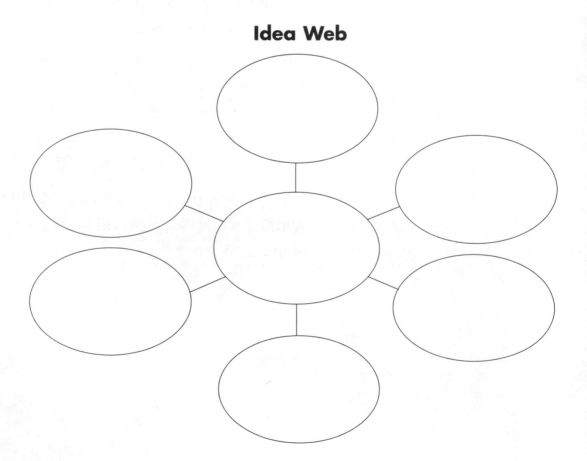

Directions Read the following steps and answer the questions.

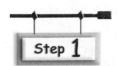

Choose a general, or broad subject.

Brainstorm to find a topic.

Write down possible topics. Then select your topic.

1. What broad subject did you use as a topic in the Idea Web?

_____

2. Where did you write the words "National Monuments"?

_____

3. What strategy did you use to choose the topic?

_____

4. Where did you write the possible topics?

_____

5. What did you do to show the topic you chose?

_____

Now that you have brainstormed for ideas and chosen a topic, you need to come up with a **central idea**. The central idea is the most important idea of the report. A strong central idea will help you keep your writing focused. What will be the central idea of your national monument report?

Directions   Read the following sample report about the Statue of Liberty.

The Statue of Liberty was a gift to the United States. It was given by France in 1884. It stood for the friendship of the two countries during the Revolutionary War. The statue stands on Liberty Island. For 100 years, people climbed the inside stairs to the top of the statue. Good and bad weather caused the statue to age. Pollution made the statue dirty and worn. In 1984, the statue was 100 years old. A group began work to clean and repair the statue. The work took two years. During the repair, the statue was covered with cloths. In 1986, a huge celebration was held. During this time, the statue was uncovered. The whole country celebrated. Lady Liberty was clean and in good condition again.

Directions   Read the steps and answer the questions.

Name the topic of the paragraph.

1. Who or what is the topic of this paragraph?

   _____

2. Describe the topic in your own words.

   _____

   _____

Find something interesting about the topic.

3. Why did the Statue of Liberty need to be cleaned and repaired?

   _____

   _____

4. What did the statue look like while it was being repaired?

   _____

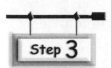

Step 3

Write a central idea about this topic. Focus on what is most important.

5. Think about the information in this report. Write a central idea for the report.

_____

_____

Ideas to Remember

> **topic**—the main subject of a piece of writing
> **central idea**—the most important idea about a topic
> **Word Web**—a graphic organizer that helps in brainstorming ideas

Apply the New Jersey CPIs

Directions   Read the two sample reports. Decide on the topic of each report. write this topic on the correct line. Think about the central idea of each report. Then write the central idea on the correct lines.

6. Long Branch is a well-known vacation spot. People like to go there because it is next to the sea. People like to swim in the sea and sunbathe on thc beaches. They also like the fresh air. Long Branch has beaches, a boardwalk, parks, and restaurants. It is a good place to spend a vacation.

Topic: _____

Central Idea: _____

7. Long Branch was once a small fishing village. In the early 1800s, people who rode stagecoaches to New York went through Long Branch. The coaches left people there. They would then take steamboats to New York. While they waited for the boats, some people decided to stay a few days in Long Branch. They enjoyed the beaches and the sea air. By the 1860s, many people were spending their vacations there. Seven presidents of the United States liked to vacation there. Many other famous people liked to visit Long Branch too. It is a town with a rich history.

Topic: _____

Central Idea: _____

Writing to Explain—Narrative

Using the picture on page 131 as a guide, write a story about what might be happening and what might happen next.

You may take notes, create a web, or do other prewriting work. Then write your narrative. Use your own paper or write in your literary response journal.

Here is a checklist for you to follow to help you do your best writing. Before you begin writing, read the checklist silently. Reread it as often as you need.

Writer's Checklist

Remember to:

❏ Keep the central idea or topic in mind.

❏ Keep your audience in mind.

❏ Support your ideas with details, explanations, and examples.

❏ Write the events of the story in a clear sequence.

❏ Include an opening and a strong ending.

❏ Use a variety of words and vary your sentence structure.

❏ Capitalize, spell, and use punctuation correctly.

❏ Write neatly.

After you write your composition, read what you have written. Use the checklist to make certain that your writing is the best it can be.

**Focus
on the
New Jersey
CCCS**

What is your favorite television cartoon? Who is the main character? What is the setting? What happens to the character? Why do these things happen? Can you answer questions like these for your own stories?

**Guided
Instruction**

There are several ways to organize your writing. One of these ways is through cause and effect. A **cause** is what makes something happen. An **effect** is what happens because of the cause. There are some helpful questions you can use to help you recognize the difference:

To find the effect, ask yourself, "What happened?"
To find the cause, ask yourself, "Why did it happen?"

The following sentence shows a cause and effect organization.

● *It snowed so much that school was canceled.*

What happened? *School was canceled.* This is the effect.
Why did it happen? *It snowed so much.* This is the cause.

Another brainstorming tool is called a **Concept Web**. Concept Webs can be used to organize ideas for your writing.

Directions   Read the sentences below and follow the steps. Then answer the questions. They will help you organize a paragraph with causes and effects.

A forest fire swept through Yellowstone National Park in 1988. There were several reasons for the fire.

1. What is the topic of this paragraph?

_____

_____

Step 1

Begin with a sentence that tells an effect.

2. Write a sentence that tells the central idea. Use your own words. Then write your sentence in the top oval of the Concept Web.

Concept Web

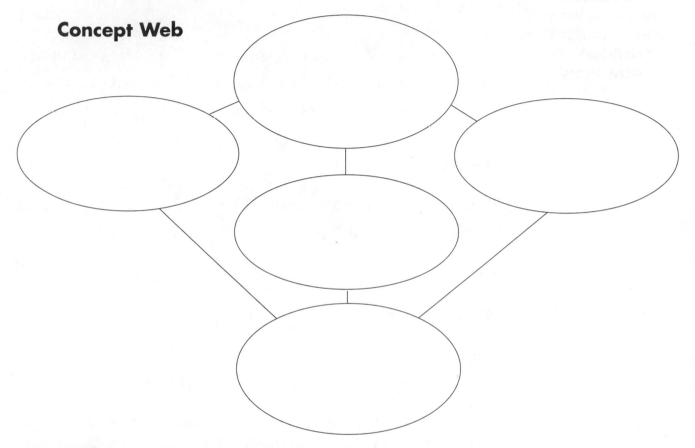

Write sentences that explain what caused this event.

3. Here are some examples of causes that explain why Yellowstone National Park had a terrible forest fire.
   ● No rain fell in Yellowstone National Park all spring and summer.
   ● Small forest fires began when lightning struck trees.
   ● The fires grew bigger and didn't die out.

4. Read the following sentences. Decide if each sentence gives a cause for the fire. Write the causes in the middle three ovals of the Concept Web.
   ● Firefighters could not control the flames.
   ● Animals needed to escape from the forest.
   ● Winds made the fires spread.
   ● There was a lack of rain.

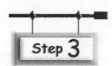

Step 3

End with a **conclusion**. Remind your readers of what the paragraph is about. Your last sentence could also give your readers a final idea to think about.

5. Decide on a conclusion, or sentence to end the paragraph. Brainstorm ideas on the lines below. Write your conclusion in the bottom oval in the Concept Web.

_____

_____

_____

_____

_____

_____

(Ideas to Remember)

Concept Web—a brainstorming tool using connected circles to organize the ideas for your writing

Apply the New Jersey CPIs

Directions   Look at the Concept Web on the next page. Read the topic sentence in the top circle. Follow the directions.

6. Think of three effects of three days of snow. Write a sentence for each effect. Write the sentences in the middle circles of the Concept Web.

7. Think of a conclusion. It should remind your readers of what the paragraph is about. Your last sentence could also give your readers a final idea to think about. Write your ending sentence in the bottom circle of the Concept Web.

Concept Web

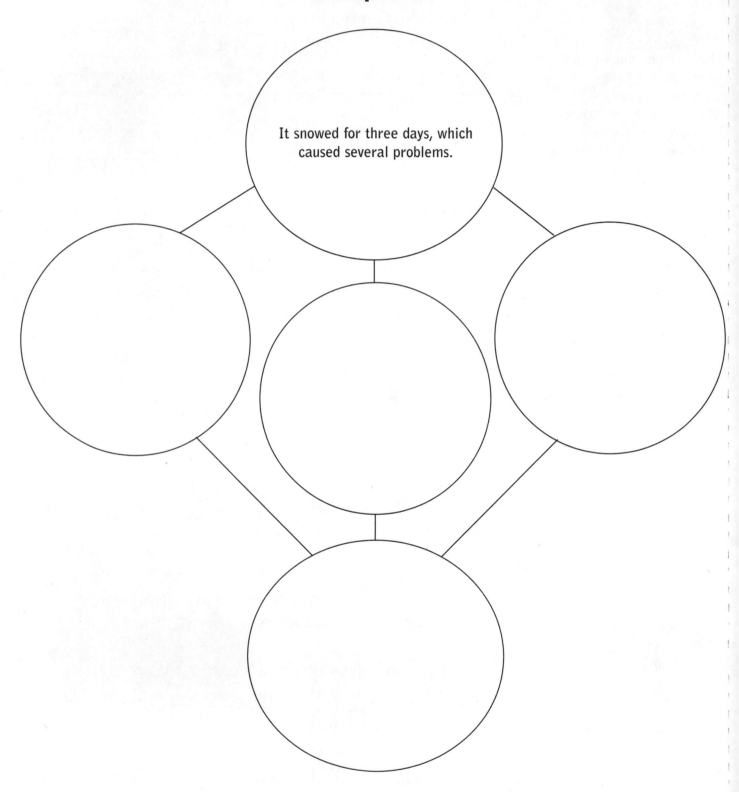

It snowed for three days, which
caused several problems.

Writing to Explain—Informational Article

Go back to the Concept Web and see if you have left out any other important information. Use the sentences and conclusion about the forest fires that you wrote. In your own words, write a paragraph that gives information about forest fires.

Here is a checklist for you to follow to help you do your best writing. Before you begin writing, read the checklist silently. Reread it as often as you need.

Writer's Checklist

Remember to:

❑ Keep the central idea or topic in mind.

❑ Keep your audience in mind.

❑ Support your ideas with details, explanations, and examples.

❑ Write the events of the story in a clear sequence.

❑ Include an opening and a strong ending.

❑ Use a variety of words and vary your sentence structure.

❑ Capitalize, spell, and use punctuation correctly.

❑ Write neatly.

After you write your composition, read what you have written. Use the checklist to make certain that your writing is the best it can be.

Focus on the New Jersey CCCS

How do you know whether your readers will like what you write? How do you know they will even understand what you have written?

Guided Instruction

Before you write, you must know your **audience**, the people who will be reading or hearing your work. If you are writing a list of rules, you must know who will read them. Will it be for people who want to use the playground safely? Will it be for people who want to use the youth center for parties? Will it be for someone who will play a game? How you write depends on who your readers will be.

Another thing to think about when you write is your reason for writing, or your **task**. Will you write safety rules to keep someone safe? Will you write rules that tell people how to use the youth center when they have parties? Will you write the rules of a game to teach people how to play?

Suppose your teacher has asked you to write a speech. It will welcome parents to parent night at school. You will give the speech at parent night. How do you write for your audience and task?

Directions Read the steps and answer the questions.

Step 1

Decide on your task for writing.

1. Why are you writing this speech?

_____

2. What do you want your listeners to know from the speech?

_____

Step 2

You must know who your audience is.

3. Who will listen to your speech?

_____

4. What will they be trying to learn by listening to your speech?

_____

_____

audience—the people who will read or hear what you write

task—what you expect your audience to learn from your writing, or your reason for writing

Directions Read the sample articles below. Then answer the questions.

Dig a hole about four inches deep. Take the plant from the pot. Set the plant and its dirt into the hole you dug. Fill in the rest of the hole with dirt you took out of it. Press the dirt around the plant firmly with your hands. After you finish planting all the plants, water them.

5. Who would be the audience for this article?

_____

If you are going on vacation soon, you might want to go to Washington, D.C. Be sure and take your family. The whole city is a lesson in history. You can see the White House, home of our President. You can watch Congress in action. Museums and memorials are everywhere you go. Your children will learn about how our government works. Spend your summer learning about our country. Visit Washington, D.C., soon.

6. Who would be the audience for this article?

_____

7. What was the writer's task for this article?

_____

Frogs are interesting animals. They have long, strong back legs. Their legs help them jump. Frogs can jump distances much longer than their bodies. These little animals live both in the water and on land. Frogs also eat bugs. Next time you have a picnic, bring a frog. They'll keep the bugs away.

8. Would the audience for this article be a science class or a music class?

   _____

9. What do you think the writer's task for this article was?

   _____

   _____

Writing to Inform—Poem

NJ ASK Practice

Directions You will be doing a writing assignment. The poem below may give you some ideas for your writing. Read the poem to yourself.

The Swing

by Robert Louis Stevenson

How do you like to go up in a swing,
   Up in the air so blue?
Oh, I do think it the pleasantest thing
   Ever a child can do!

Up in the air and over the wall,
   Till I can see so wide,
Rivers and trees and cattle and all
   Over the countryside —

Till I look down on the garden green,
   Down on the roof so brown —
Up in the air I go flying again,
   Up in the air and down!

The person who wrote this poem loved to swing. Sometimes it's a lot easier to write about things you like. Imagine your task is to write a poem about your favorite thing to do after school. Using the questions below as a guide, brainstorm some ideas on a separate sheet of paper about your favorite after-school activity. When you have finished brainstorming, write the most important details into full sentences. Arrange your sentences in a logical order.

- **When do you get to do your favorite activity?**
- **What do you like most about your favorite activity?**
- **Why is this your favorite activity?**
- **How does this activity make you feel?**
- **Do you do this activity with other people?**
- **Would other people like doing it? Why?**

You may take notes, create a web, or do other prewriting work. Then write your sentences. Use your own paper or write in your literary response journal.

Here is a checklist for you to follow to help you do your best writing. Before you begin writing, read the checklist silently. Reread it as often as you need.

Writer's Checklist

Remember to:

❒ Keep the central idea or topic in mind.

❒ Keep your audience in mind.

❒ Support your ideas with details, explanations, and examples.

❒ Write the sentences in a clear sequence.

❒ Use a variety of words and vary your sentence structure.

❒ State your opinion or conclusion clearly.

❒ Capitalize, spell, and use punctuation correctly.

❒ Write neatly.

After you write your sentences, read what you have written. Use the checklist to make certain that your writing is the best it can be.

Focus on the New Jersey CCCS

Have you ever used a map? What did you use it for? There are different kinds of maps. How are directions like maps? How can a list of ideas might be a map for a story or report? How can this kind of map help you arrange your ideas in a logical order?

Guided Instruction

You are going to write a paragraph. A **paragraph** is a group of sentences that explains one topic or main idea. What do you want to say in your paragraph? What is a good **prewriting** exercise to use? Think about the following ideas.

- Think of an opening for your paragraph. What should it say? Many writers tell their audience what their purpose is.
- Keep your main idea in mind. Choose details that best explain your central idea. Make sure you don't write any unnecessary details.
- Choose a closing. It should help you meet your purpose for writing. The closing can sum up the point you want to make.

Make a list of the ideas you want to present. When your plan is complete, use these points to write sentences. Then put the sentences into a paragraph. A **chart** is a good prewriting tool.

Directions Read the information listed in the graphic organizer.
Think about the way the writer states ideas. Then follow the directions.

Organize Writing to Persuade

Opening Sentence

My favorite place in New Jersey is the Palisades.

Main Idea

High cliffs along the Hudson River are fun to visit.

Details	Examples
high and beautiful area	cliffs carved out during Ice Age
Palisades in danger of being destroyed	blasted around 1900 for rocks used in buildings
saved by women of New Jersey	pushed people to the Palisades' beauty worked to get laws passed to protect cliffs
great activities	Allison Park, Fort Lee Park, museum, hiking, picnic area

Closing Sentence

If you enjoy having a great time, visit the Palisades.

Step 1

Write an opening that tells your purpose for writing.

1. What does this writer want readers to know about the Palisades?

_____

_____

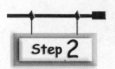

Step 2

Tell the main idea you want to present about your topic.

2. What point will all the details support?

_____

_____

Step 3

List details for each paragraph you will write.

3. How does the writer support the main idea?

_____

_____

_____

4. Why does the writer list examples for each detail?

_____

_____

Step 4

Write a closing that sums up what you want to say or tells how you feel about your topic.

5. What does the closing urge readers to do?

_____

_____

Ideas to Remember

opening—the beginning of a paragraph

main idea—the main point that the writer has to make about the subject

closing—the ending of a paragraph; the writer may restate the central idea and give his or her own views about the subject

Directions Now you will fill in your own chart to plan a paragraph about Molly Pitcher. Read the following facts. Use the facts to complete the graphic organizer.

- bravely fought in the Revolutionary War
- a battle in New Jersey
- 1775
- carried water to the soldiers
- wounded husband fell
- took his place
- helped fire the cannons
- still remembered

Sequencing List

Opening Sentence
Main Idea
First Detail
Second Detail
Third Detail
Closing

Writing to Explain—Paragraph

Now take the ideas you have written in the chart and turn them into sentences for a paragraph. Write your paragraph on the lines below.

_____

_____

_____

_____

_____

_____

_____

Writer's Checklist

Remember to:

❏ Keep the central idea or topic in mind.

❏ Keep your audience in mind.

❏ Support your ideas with details, explanations, and examples.

❏ State your ideas in a clear sequence.

❏ Include an opening and a closing.

❏ Use a variety of words and vary your sentence structure.

❏ State your opinion or conclusion clearly.

❏ Capitalize, spell, and use punctuation correctly.

❏ Write neatly.

After you write your paragraph, read what you have written. Use the checklist to make certain that your writing is the best it can be.

Focus on the New Jersey CCCS

Think of a story that you recently told someone. How did you tell this story? Did you describe the actions in a certain order? Did you use words that made your listener feel like he or she were there?

Guided Instruction

The first time you write a paper, it is called a draft. What is a draft like? It is your work in a rough form. When you write a draft, you only put your ideas down on paper. Later you will go back to correct and improve your work.

Think about what makes good writing. This will make it easier to correct and improve your writing later. What are some elements of good writing? Keep these four important ideas in mind as you write your draft.

- **Good Form** — What form should you use for your writing? Make it fit your purpose. Should you write a letter, an article, or another form of writing?

- **Clear Central Idea** — Is your central idea easy to understand? do your details explain the central idea?

- **Strong Opening and Closing** — Have you used opening and closing sentences? Do they help your reader understand your main point?

- **Strong Descriptive Words** — Are your ideas easy to understand? Do you say things in creative and interesting ways?

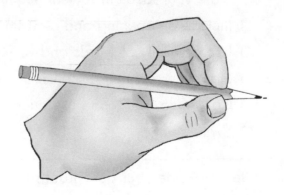

Directions Read the sample draft below. Think about the ideas in it. Follow the steps and answer the questions.

Paul Robeson didn't waste a minute of his long life. Robeson was born in Princeton, New Jersey, in 1898. He went to Rutgers University. He played four sports. Robeson made All-American in football. He earned this honor twice. At Columbia, he got a degree in law. Then he became an actor and singer.

Robeson also spoke out for peace and justice. He wanted to help other African Americans. Some people didn't like what he said. Robeson was not allowed to leave the United States for eight years. But he never stopped saying what he believed.

Step 1

Decide on your purpose for writing.

1. What is the topic of this rough draft?

   _____

2. Is this rough draft in the form of a story? Is it in the form of an article?

   _____

3. Will readers understand the point this writer is trying to make? Explain your answer.

   _____

   _____

   _____

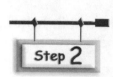

Decide whether you have used elements of good writing.

4. What is the opening sentence of this draft?

_____

5. What is the central idea of the rough draft?

_____

6. What does this writer think about his or her topic?

_____

_____

Set a plan for writing your rough draft.

7. Why should you think about the elements of writing as you write a rough draft?

_____

_____

_____

Ideas to Remember

draft—a rough form of writing

Apply the New Jersey CPIs

Directions Suppose you have been assigned to write a paper. The topic is the best movie you have ever seen. Answer the following questions. They will help you plan your writing.

8. What will be the topic of your paper?

    _____

9. What will be the central idea of your paper? What is the main point you want to make about the movie?

    _____

10. How will you state your ideas about the movie?

    _____

11. What will be the opening sentence of your paper?

    _____

12. What are some details that you will use to explain the central idea about the movie?

    _____

13. What idea will be the closing of your paper?

    _____

Writing to Explain—Your Favorite Movie

You have been hired by your local newspaper to write a brief review of your favorite movie. Using the answers you gave in the previous exercise, write a review of this movie. It should be at least three paragraphs long. Think about the following questions.

- Is the movie funny, serious, informative, or realistic?
- Who are the main characters in this movie?
- What are the characters like?
- What is your favorite part of the movie?
- Is there a problem that gets resolved at the end?

You may take notes, create a web, or do other prewriting work. Then write your narrative. Use your own paper or write in your literary response journal.

Here is a checklist for you to follow to help you do your best writing. Before you begin writing, read the checklist silently. Reread it as often as you need.

Writer's Checklist

Remember to:

❒ Keep the central idea or topic in mind.

❒ Keep your audience in mind.

❒ Support your ideas with details, explanations, and examples.

❒ State your ideas in a clear sequence.

❒ Include an opening and a closing.

❒ Use a variety of words and vary your sentence structure.

❒ State your opinion or conclusion clearly.

❒ Capitalize, spell, and use punctuation correctly.

❒ Write neatly.

After you write your composition, read what you have written. Use the checklist to make certain that your writing is the best it can be.

Focus on the New Jersey CCCS

When you hear voices in a crowd, what do they sound like? Can you understand everything that everyone says? Why is it important for you to write clearly? How do you know a reader can understand what you write?

Guided Instruction

As a writer, it is very important to **reread** everything you have written. How do you **revise**, or check your writing? There are some key things to look for when you revise. First, check for **clear wording.** Sentences that are worded badly can confuse your readers. Make sure that what you have written says exactly what you mean to say. Don't choose words that have unclear meanings.

Next, check for proper **organization** of ideas. Write about events in the order in which they happened. If you are not writing about events, use an **outline** to put your ideas in order. Be sure that the order is clear and easy to follow. If events or ideas are written out of order, readers can be confused.

What are some effective ways to check your writing for clear wording and good organization? Read the following paragraph. Think about how this writer worded and organized this piece of writing.

Ruth Saint Denis loved the art of dancing. Several other dancers learned to dance at their school. She was one of the greatest American dancers born in Newark, New Jersey. In the early 1900s, Ruth danced in many ballets. Some were set in Egypt and Japan. She wanted more people to enjoy the art of dancing. She and her husband started a school of dance.

Directions Follow the steps and answer the questions.

Step 1

Think about
your ideas and
organization as
you check
your writing.

1. What do you do when you check your writing?

   _____

2. What is clear wording?

   _____

3. How should your writing be organized?

   _____

   _____

Step 2

Check to see
that your writing
is clear.

4. Reread the paragraph. The third sentence sives the wrong
   idea. What is unclear about this sentence?

   _____

   _____

5. Why is this sentence unclear?

   _____

   _____

6. Rewrite the sentence into two sentences. (Hint: be sure one
   of the sentences shows that Ruth Saint Denis was **born** in
   Newark, New Jersey.)

   _____

   _____

Step 3

Check to see
that your writing
is clear.

7. Who learned to dance at Ruth's school?

_____

8. Where is this idea found in the paragraph?

_____

9. Why should this idea be moved to another spot in the
paragraph? Where should it be placed?

_____

_____

 Ideas to Remember

clear wording—wording that says exactly what a writer
wants to say

organization—the order in which ideas are presented in
written work

Directions Read the paragraph below. Then rewrite it to make the wording clearer. Change the order of the sentences if you need to. (Hint: Some sentences won't have to be changed.)

Yesterday Justin fell off his skateboard onto the sidewalk. She came running out of her house. His mother saw him fall from her kitchen window. She helped him get up. Then he walked into his house. He picked up his skateboard.

_____

_____

_____

_____

_____

Writing to Explain—Narrative

Using the picture on page 159 as a guide, write a story about what might be happening and what might happen next.

You may take notes, create a web, or do other prewriting work. Then write your narrative. Use your own paper or write in your literary response journal.

Here is a checklist for you to follow to help you do your best writing. Before you begin writing, read the checklist silently as it is read to you. Reread it as often as you need.

Writer's Checklist

Remember to:

❐ Keep the central idea or topic in mind.

❐ Keep your audience in mind.

❐ Support your ideas with details, explanations, and examples.

❐ State your ideas in a clear sequence.

❐ Include an opening and a closing.

❐ Use a variety of words and vary your sentence structure.

❐ State your opinion or conclusion clearly.

❐ Capitalize, spell, and use punctuation correctly.

❐ Write neatly.

After you write your composition, read what you have written. Use the checklist to make certain that your writing is the best it can be.

Focus on the New Jersey CCCS

Why are there different kinds of sentences? How do they work in communication? How do questions and statements work in communication?

Guided Instruction

As a writer, nearly everything that you will will be put into **sentences**. Sentences can do so many different things. Some sentences give orders. Others ask questions or express exclamations. Still others give information. The ways that sentences work are endless. Look at the four sentences below.

1. Did you know that African gray parrots are almost as smart as humans?

2. Pet parrots need love and attention or they get sick.

3. What a beautiful bird that is!

4. Put some fresh water out for the parrot to drink.

Now let's look at how these sentences work.

Which sentence asks a question? Sentence 1 is an **interrogative** sentence. It asks a question. It ends with a question mark.

Which sentence gives information? Sentence 2 is a **declarative** sentence. It gives information to the reader. It ends with a period.

Which sentence shows strong feeling? Sentence 3 is an **exclamatory** sentence. It ends with an exclamation point.

Which sentence tells someone to do something? Sentence 4 is an **imperative** sentence. It also ends with a period. But notice that there is no subject. The subject *you* is understood as the person or thing the speaker is communicating with.

Directions Read the sentences below. Then follow the steps and answer the questions.

1. Don't slip on the ice.

2. I can't find my hat!

3. Is anyone going sledding?

4. I need to walk down to the post office.

Find the sentence that gives information in a statement.

1. Which of these four sentences gives information in a statement?

_____

2. What is the end punctuation for this sentence?

_____

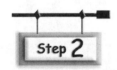

Find the sentence that asks a question.

3. Which sentence asks a question?

_____

4. What is the end punctuation?

_____

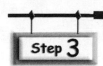

Step 3

Find the sentence that makes a strong statement.

5. Which sentence might be shouted?

_____

6. What is the end punctuation for this sentence?

_____

Step 4

Find the sentence that tells someone to do something.

7. Which sentence gives an order?

_____

8. What is the end punctuation for this sentence?

_____

Ideas to Remember

> **declarative**—a sentence that gives information; it ends with a period (.)
>
> **interrogative**—a sentence that asks a question; it ends with a question mark (?)
>
> **imperative**—a sentence that tells someone to do something; it usually ends with a period (.)
>
> **exclamatory**—a sentence that makes a strong statement; it ends with an exclamation point (!)

Apply the New Jersey CPIs

Directions Now you will try to rewrite some sentences on your own. Read each sentence below. Then look at the word that follows each sentence in parentheses. This word will tell you the style you should use for your rewrite. For example, if the word says *Interrogative* you will rewrite the sentence into a question. Be sure to use the correct punctuation.

9. You would answer the phone late at night. (Interrogative)

_____

10. Did the police want my Aunt Grace to raise a bird? (Declarative)

_____

11. Did some horrible person cut Lucy's wing feathers? (Exclamatory)

_____

12. That is why she couldn't fly. (Interrogative)

_____

13. Maybe you can teach Lucy to sing a song. (Imperative)

_____

14. Do Lucy and Aunt Grace have a garden on the patio? (Declarative)

_____

15. When you give her fresh water, will you give Lucy a bath? (Imperative)

_____

16. Do not open the cage door. (Exclamatory)

_____

Writing to Describe—Personal Narrative

Many people love to read books. Some people like books about animals. Others love mysteries. Many people like books about sports heroes or musicians. What kind of books do you like? Describe the kind of books you enjoy reading. Give details telling why you like that kind of book.

- What kinds of books do you like to read?
- Name some of your favorite books.
- What did you like about these books?
- How did the books make you feel when you were reading them?
- What is one of your favorite scenes from a book?

You may take notes, create a web, or do other prewriting work. Then write your narrative. Use your own paper or write in your literary response journal.

Here is a checklist for you to follow to help you do your best writing. Before you begin writing, read the checklist silently. Reread it as often as you need.

Writer's Checklist

Remember to:

❏ Keep the central idea or topic in mind.

❏ Keep your audience in mind.

❏ Support your ideas with details, explanations, and examples.

❏ State your ideas in a clear sequence.

❏ Include an opening and a closing.

❏ Use a variety of words and vary your sentence structure.

❏ State your opinion or conclusion clearly.

❏ Capitalize, spell, and use punctuation correctly.

❏ Write neatly.

After you write your composition, read what you have written. Use the checklist to make certain that your writing is the best it can be.

Focus on the New Jersey CCCS

Are basketball and hoops the same game? When you shoot hoops are you playing basketball? Why do you think there is often more than one name for the same thing?

Guided Instruction

Good writers keep their work interesting. They are careful about **word choice**. They use different kinds of words. How many words can you think of that mean *car*? You might list the words *automobile* or *vehicle*.

Directions Read the following sentences. Then follow the steps and answer the questions.

1. In 1775, American soldiers **worked** for freedom from Great Britain.
2. George Washington's men **went** across the Delaware River to get to Trenton.

Step 1

Find any words that are overused or not very interesting.

1. Look at sentence 1. Look at the word in **bold** letters. Does it make the sentence interesting? Why or why not?

_____

_____

2. Look at sentence 2. Look at the word in bold letters. Does it make the sentence interesting? Why or why not?

_____

_____

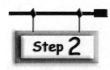

Step 2

Find different words that are more interesting.

3. In sentence 1, which word might replace **worked**? Fill in the circle beside the answer that you choose.

   Ⓐ sang

   Ⓑ fought

   Ⓒ ran

   Ⓓ looked

Step 3

Find words that mean what you want to say.

4. In sentence 2, which word might replace **went**? Fill in the circle beside the answer that you choose.

   Ⓐ rowed

   Ⓑ sailed

   Ⓒ floated

   Ⓓ crossed

5. Explain why you chose that word for question 4.

_____

_____

(Ideas to Remember)

word choice—to make writing interesting by using different words that are not overused, or words that are specific

Apply the New Jersey CPIs

Directions Read the following sentences. Think about the word in bold letters. Look at the four words below each sentence. Circle the word in each group that has the same meaning, but would be more interesting.

6. During the Revolutionary war, Americans **held** Tammany Day on May 1.

   touched   caught   celebrated   sold

7. Tammany Day **remembered** Chief Tammany of the Lenni-Lenape Nation.

   honored   recalled   memorized   caught

8. The Lenni-Lenape were the first people to **live** on lands that became New Jersey, Delaware, and Pennsylvania.

   be   walk   settle   travel

9. Chief Tammany **helped** Europeans who moved to this place in the late 1600s.

   fixed   aided   fought   paid

Writing to Explain—Letter

Write a letter to your teacher. Explain what you learned in school this week. Describe different events from school and your homework. Be sure to use words that make your meaning clear.

- What subjects did you learn during the week?
- List the order in which you want to present your ideas.
- What different subjects did you enjoy? Why?
- What different subjects did you not enjoy? Why?
- Did you have homework for all your classes?
- What homework did you enjoy doing? Why?
- What homework did you not enjoy doing? Why?
- Did you learn anything in your physical education class or at recess?

You may take notes, create a web, or do other prewriting work. Then write your letter. Use your own paper or write in your literary response journal.

Here is a checklist for you to follow to help you do your best writing. Before you begin writing, read the checklist silently as it is read to you. Reread it as often as you need.

Writer's Checklist

Remember to:

❑ Keep the central idea or topic in mind.

❑ Keep your audience in mind.

❑ Support your ideas with details, explanations, and examples.

❑ State your ideas in a clear sequence.

❑ Include an opening and a closing.

❑ Use a variety of words and vary your sentence structure.

❑ State your opinion or conclusion clearly.

❑ Capitalize, spell, and use punctuation correctly.

❑ Write neatly.

After you write your composition, read what you have written. Use the checklist to make certain that your writing is the best it can be.

Focus on the New Jersey CCCS

Have you ever watched an adult drive a car? What do drivers do when they change lanes? How is a writer like a driver of a car? What do writers do when they change ideas? How do they show a change in ideas?

Guided Instruction

Good drivers signal when they are changing lanes. Writers also signal when they are changing ideas. Writers begin a new **paragraph** when they change ideas. To show that they have started a new paragraph, they indent the first line. To **indent** means to set the first word of the new paragraph slightly to the right of the rest of the paragraph. The first line then looks as if it has a "dent" in it.

Read the paragraphs below and look at the picture on page 170.

Knitting is a very old craft. In early times, knitting was a job for men. Men in the Middle East traveled everywhere by camel. As they swayed across the desert on the back of their camels, they knitted. They knitted cloth for clothing. They knitted cloth for tents. They knitted rough cloth for useful things. They also knitted fine cloth for beautiful things. In other cultures, men were always the people who knitted cloth for clothing and other things.

Today, most knitting is done by women. Many grown-ups still have pictures in their minds of their grandmothers knitting. In the early 1900s, women knitted socks for their husbands, sons, and other men in the family. Most sweaters were knit by hand. Wives, mothers, and daughters made knitted clothing for the family. Now, however, we buy most of our clothes from stores. To get a hand-knit sweater from someone is a rare gift.

Directions Follow the steps. Answer the questions.

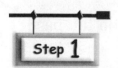

Step 1

Find the main idea of a paragraph.

1. What is the first paragraph talking about?

   _____

2. What is the second paragraph talking about?

   _____

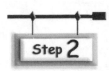

Find the details that support the topic of a paragraph.

3. Write three details from the first paragraph that support the main idea.

_____

_____

_____

_____

4. Write three details from the second paragraph that support the main idea.

_____

_____

_____

_____

Find where the writer changes ideas.

5. How does the writer change ideas?

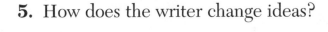

_____

6. How does the writer show the shift of ideas on the page?

_____

Ideas to Remember

paragraph—a group of sentences that present a main idea and the details that support it

indent—to move the beginning words of a paragraph to the right of the rest of the paragraph so that a dent is created in the first line

Apply the New Jersey CPIs

Directions Use the Idea Webs to complete this exercise. Read the following sentences. Decide which two sentences are main ideas. Write them in the center ovals. Then find the details that support each one. Add ovals for each one. Rewrite the sentences on a separate sheet of paper so that they form two paragraphs. Be sure to indent each paragraph as you write.

- I also love art festivals.
- I put feathers around the eyes.
- I also like to see all the baking and cooking contests.
- I love to go to country fairs.
- Then I cannot only see and smell all the pies, bread, and cookies—I can taste them, too.
- I get to make my own art there, too.
- Someday I want to judge a baking contest.
- Every year I get my face painted at the kids' art booth.
- One of my favorite artists is the glass blower.
- People bring mostly farm animals to fairs to be judged.
- I like to see all the drawings and paintings.
- I like to visit the animal barns to see all the animals.
- I got a glass sun catcher for my window.
- Last year I made a mask.

Idea Web—Paragraph 1

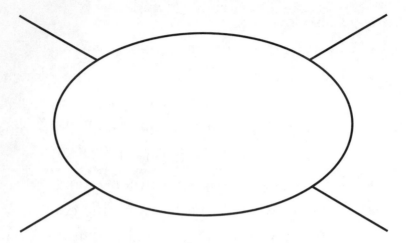

Idea Web—Paragraph 2

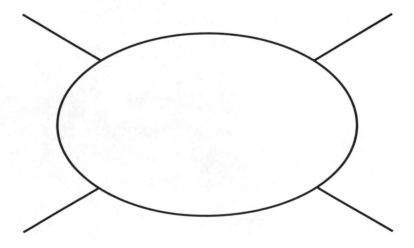

Writing to Explain—Narrative

**NJ ASK
Practice**

Today you will do a writing assignment. The poem below, "Oops!," may give you ideas for your writing. Read the poem to yourself while it is read to you.

Oops!
by Bruce Lansky

Three coffee cups my mother loved
lie shattered on the floor.
Three ripe tomatoes splattered
when they hit the kitchen door.

Three jumbo eggs are scrambled.
But they're not on a plate.
Three loaves of bread are crumbled.
I'll use the crumbs for bait.

Three Barbie dolls have lost their heads.
Three pepper mills are smashed.
Three goldfish died while doing flips.
Three model airplanes crashed.

Three lettuce heads unraveled.
Three onions came unpeeled.
My parents didn't know who did it
till my sister squealed.

My parents are befuddled.
They think that I've gone nuts.
But there's a simpler explanation:
I'm a juggling klutz.

In his poem, Bruce Lansky talks about all the things he has broken while trying to juggle. Think about something that you worked at trying to learn. Explain what you were trying to learn and how other people felt about it. Think about the following points.

- **What were you trying to learn?**
- **What did you do when trying?**
- **How long did it take you to learn?**
- **How did your family feel about what you were doing?**
- **When did you know you had met your goal?**

You may take notes, create a web, or do other prewriting work. Then write your narrative. Use your own paper or write in your literary response journal.

Here is a checklist for you to follow to help you do your best writing. Before you begin writing, read the checklist silently as it is read to you. Reread it as often as you need.

Writer's Checklist

Remember to:

❏ Keep the central idea or topic in mind.

❏ Keep your audience in mind.

❏ Support your ideas with details, explanations, and examples.

❏ State your ideas in a clear sequence.

❏ Include an opening and a closing.

❏ Use a variety of words and vary your sentence structure.

❏ State your opinion or conclusion clearly.

❏ Capitalize, spell, and use punctuation correctly.

❏ Write neatly.

After you write your composition, read what you have written. Use the checklist to make certain that your writing is the best it can be.

Focus on the New Jersey CCCS

Do you have trouble spelling some words? What can you do to keep from misspelling the same words each time you try to write them?

Guided Instruction

It is important to **proofread**, or check, your writing. What should you look for? Are there any spelling errors? You may not be sure about how to spell a word. In this case, try to look it up in the dictionary. Here are some commonly misspelled words and tips for remembering how they are spelled.

cellar	This word is spelled *ar* not *er*.
chief	Follow the rule, *i* before *e* except after *c*.
develop	Say this word carefully to spell it correctly.
dictionary	The end of the word is spelled *ary* not *ery*.
eighth	The letters *eigh* spell the *a* sound.
grammar	The word ends with *ar* not *er*.
misspelled	Don't forget the second *s* and the second *l*.
weird	This word is spelled *ei*, not *ie*. This word does not follow the rule about *i* before *e*.
receive	This word is spelled with an *ei*. This word follows the rule about *i* before *e* except after *c*.
address	Don't forget the double *d* and double *s*.

To correct a misspelled word, use an editing mark, called a carat.

For example: ~~recieve~~ receive
          ^

Directions   Read the paragraph below. Follow the steps and answer the questions.

An important part of the writing process is proofreding. I always keep a dictionery nearby. That way I can check my writing for mispelled words. Sometimes I make careless or wierd mistakes. My teacher says my cheif weakness in proofreading is that I rush. If I learned to proofread more carefully, I would recieve better grades.

Step 1

Find the misspelled words in the paragraph.

1. Reread the first sentence in the paragraph. What word is misspelled?

_____

2. What is the correct spelling of this word?

_____

3. What word is misspelled in the second sentence?

_____

4. What is the correct spelling of this word?

_____

5. What other words have been misspelled in the paragraph?

_____

6. How should these words be spelled?

_____

Step 2

Mark the misspelled words correctly.

7. Which is the correct way to mark a misspelled word? Fill in the circle beside the answer you choose.

 **Ideas to Remember**

misspelled words—words that are spelled incorrectly
proofread—check writing for mistakes

Apply the New Jersey CPIs

This is a list of commonly confused words. Read each one and notice how they are different. Check your writing for them when you proofread.

accept   to take or receive
except   other than

for   a preposition meaning *because* or *directed to*
four   the number 4

forth   forward or out
fourth   that which comes after third and before fifth

quite   completely or entirely
quiet   the opposite of *noisy*

then   at the time or moment
than   used in comparison

whose   shows ownership
who's   the contraction for *who is*

your   shows ownership
you're   the contraction for *you are*

Directions Read the following sentences. Words that are commonly confused are underlined. One of the underlined words in each sentence is incorrect. Cross it out. Mark a carat underneath it. Write the correct word above the mistake.

8. I will <u>except</u> the packages for you. <u>Then</u> I will deliver them to you.

9. <u>Who's</u> book is this? Is this <u>your</u> book?

10. I am the <u>fourth</u> person in line. <u>Your</u> the fifth person in line.

11. It is <u>quiet</u> noisy in here. Please try to be <u>quiet</u>.

12. Everyone <u>accept</u> for Danny is here. He is <u>quite</u> late.

13. Let's go to <u>your</u> house first. <u>Than</u> we can go to the park.

14. I am older <u>then</u> you. You're only seven years old.

15. Come <u>fourth</u> and tell the truth. Do you know <u>whose</u> money this is?

16. I am in the <u>forth</u> grade. <u>You're</u> in the same grade as I am.

17. Can I borrow <u>for</u> apples? My mother needs them <u>for</u> a pie.

Writing to Entertain—Story

Look at the picture and tell a story about it. Before you write, think about the following questions.

- **Who are the characters?**
- **What are their names?**
- **What are the characters doing?**
- **What is the setting of the story?**
- **Do the characters say anything?**
- **Is this a realistic or fictional story?**
- **Is the story funny or serious?**

You may take notes, create a web, or do other prewriting work. Then write your narrative. Use your own paper or write in your literary response journal.

Here is a checklist for you to follow to help you do your best writing. Before you begin writing, read the checklist silently.

Writer's Checklist

Remember to:

- ❏ Keep the central idea or topic in mind.
- ❏ Keep your audience in mind.
- ❏ Support your ideas with details, explanations, and examples.
- ❏ State your ideas in a clear sequence.
- ❏ Include an opening and a closing.
- ❏ Use a variety of words and vary your sentence structure.
- ❏ State your opinion or conclusion clearly.
- ❏ Capitalize, spell, and use punctuation correctly.
- ❏ Write neatly.

After you write your composition, read what you have written. Use the checklist to make certain that your writing is the best it can be.

Focus on the New Jersey CCCS

What is the purpose of a book's table of contents? Without a table of contents, how could you tell where one chapter ended and another started? How are capital letters like a table of contents?

Guided Instruction

Check for **capitalization** as you edit your writing. Always capitalize the first letter of the first word of a sentence. Also, capitalize the first letter of any proper noun. **Proper nouns** name a specific person, place, or thing.

Editors use editing marks to show what changes need to be made on a page. The editing mark for capitalization is three short lines under each letter that is to be capitalized. See the example below:

the empire state building
≡   ≡   ≡

Directions Read the following paragraph. Notice that there are no capital letters. Think about which words need to be capitalized. Follow the steps. Answer the questions.

mrs. hernandez has seen a lot of changes. she's lived in new jersey a long time. she and her husband came from cuba in june of 1960. they started an eating place called good eats in weehawken. there were not many tables, but people loved their food. now they serve hundreds of people monday through saturday.

Step 1

Make sure each sentence begins with a capital letter.

1. Look at the first sentence. What is wrong with the first name?

_____

2. How should the first name in this sentence be written?

_____

3. What other sentence beginning words need to be capitalized? Write them wth correct capital letters.

_____

Step 2

Make sure the names of people begin with a capital letter.

4. What person is named in the first sentence?

_____

5. What letters in this person's name should be capitalized?

_____

6. Write this person's name with correct capital letters.

_____

Step 3

Make sure the names of specific places and things begin with a capital letter.

7. Look at the second sentence. What specific place is named? It is a proper noun. Write it with the correct capital letters.

_____

8. Look at the third sentence. What two words are proper nouns? Write them with the correct capital letters.

_____

9. Look at the rest of the paragraph. What other proper names should be capitalized? Write them with the correct capital letters.

_____

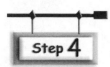

Step 4

Use editing marks to show capitalization.

10. What is the correct editing mark to show that a letter should be capitalized?

_____

11. Mark letters that should be capitals in the paragraph. Use editing marks.

_____

_____

_____

Ideas to Remember

edit for capitalization—capitalize the first word in a sentence and all proper nouns

Apply the New Jersey CPIs

Directions Read the paragraph below. Which letters should be changed to capital letters? Mark them. The first one is done for you.

12. an important leader was killed in the persian gulf war. major marie rossi of oradell, new jersey, flew a helicopter. she took part in battles when the u.s. pushed iraq out of kuwait in 1991. she was the first american woman to lead soldiers in a war. major rossi was killed at the end of the war. the city of oradell built a monument in her honor in 1992. people will always remember this brave hero, marie rossi.

Writing to Record—Diary Entry

**NJ ASK
Practice**

Many people write in diaries. They describe what has happened to them each day. They tell how they feel about daily events. Think about what has happened to you today. Write a diary entry describing your day.

- **What did you do today?**
- **Have you had a good day or a bad day? What made it good or bad?**
- **Was there someone you enjoyed talking with today? Describe the person.**
- **What, if anything, would you have changed about today?**

You may take notes, create a web, or do other prewriting work. Then write your diary entry. Use your own paper or write in your literary response journal.

Here is a checklist for you to follow to help you do your best writing. Before you begin writing, read the checklist silently as it is read to you. Reread it as often as you need.

Writer's Checklist

Remember to:

❏ Keep the central idea or topic in mind.

❏ Keep your audience in mind.

❏ Support your ideas with details, explanations, and examples.

❏ State your ideas in a clear sequence.

❏ Include an opening and a closing.

❏ Use a variety of words and vary your sentence structure.

❏ State your opinion or conclusion clearly.

❏ Capitalize, spell, and use punctuation correctly.

❏ Write neatly.

After you write your composition, read what you have written. Use the checklist to make certain that your writing is the best it can be.

Focus
on the
New Jersey
CCCS
What kinds of marks are at the ends of sentences? Do these marks mean different things? When is the best time to use each one? Why do you need to use punctuation marks?

**Guided
Instruction**

Always **proofread** your writing for correct punctuation. **Punctuation marks** are designed to make a sentence clear for the reader, so that its meaning can be understood. They also help explain how a sentence should be read. Read the examples below.

End Marks

- Put a **period** (.) at the end of a sentence that is a statement.

    I looked at my watch.

- Put a **question mark** (?) at the end of a sentence that asks a question.

    Do you know what time it is?
    ⋀

- Put an **exclamation point** (!) at the end of a sentence that shows great feeling or surprise.

    Wow, it's late!
    ⋀

Directions Read the sentences below. Use these as you follow the steps and answer the questions.

A Watch out

B That boy is my younger brother

C Can you help me with my homework

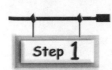

Step 1

Fix any problems with periods at the ends of sentences.

1. What kind of sentence ends with a period?

_____

2. Look at the sentences. Which sentence is a statement?

_____

3. Add a period to the end of this sentence.

Step 2

Fix any problems with question marks at the ends of sentences.

4. What kind of sentence ends with a question mark?

_____

5. Look at the sentences. Which sentence asks a question?

_____

6. Add a question mark to the end of this sentence.

Step 3

Fix any problems with exclamation points at the ends of sentences.

7. What kind of sentence ends with an exclamation point?

_____

8. Look at the sentences. Which sentence shows great feeling or surprise?

_____

9. Add an exclamation point to the end of this sentence.

Ideas to Remember

edit end punctuation—always check to see that you've used periods, question marks, and exclamation points correctly in your writing

period—punctuation mark at the end of a sentence that is a statement

question mark—punctuation mark at the end of a sentence that asks a question

exclamation point—punctuation mark at the end of a sentence that shows great feeling or surprise

Apply the New Jersey CPIs

Directions Read each sentence below. Decide what kind of sentence it is. Add the correct end punctuation.

10. How many books did you borrow from the library

11. During the summer we went on a vacation

12. I would like a hamburger for dinner

13. Oh no, a tornado is coming

14. Did you see that new movie

15. My dog likes to sleep in my room

16. My new bicycle is awesome

17. Can you see the hot air balloon

18. I want a computer game for Christmas

Writing to Entertain—Narrative

Think about what it would be like to be the president of the United States. Being the president is a very important job. As president, you must make major decisions that affect millions of people. Imagine you are the president for a day. Write a story about one day in your life.

- **What major event happened that day?**
- **What people were involved in the event?**
- **What decision did you have to make about the event?**
- **How did you feel as you were trying to make your decision?**
- **What happened as a result of your decision?**

You may take notes, create a web, or do other prewriting work. Then write your narrative. Use your own paper or write in your literary response journal.

Here is a checklist for you to follow to help you do your best writing. Before you begin writing, read the checklist silently. Reread it as often as you need.

Writer's Checklist

Remember to:

- ❏ Keep the central idea or topic in mind.
- ❏ Keep your audience in mind.
- ❏ Support your ideas with details, explanations, and examples.
- ❏ State your ideas in a clear sequence.
- ❏ Include an opening and a closing.
- ❏ Use a variety of words and vary your sentence structure.
- ❏ State your opinion or conclusion clearly.
- ❏ Capitalize, spell, and use punctuation correctly.
- ❏ Write neatly.

After you write your composition, read what you have written. Use the checklist to make certain that your writing is the best it can be.

Focus on the New Jersey CCCS

What is the difference between singular and plural? How do you change a singular noun into a plural noun?

Guided Instruction

A **singular noun** names one person, place, or thing. A **plural noun** names more than one person, place, or thing. Before you try to change a singular noun into a plural, first look at the way it is spelled. You can make a **regular noun** plural just by adding an -*s* or an -*es* to the end of it. **Irregular nouns** are not so easy. Look at the chart on the next page. It will help you recognize some common regular and irregular nouns, and show you how to make them plural.

Use this chart to know how to form both regular and irregular plurals.

Rule for forming plural	Example
For most regular nouns, add *s* at the end.	stick–sticks, plate–plates
For most words ending in *f*, *fe*, or *ff*, add *s* only.	roof–roofs, safe–safes, sheriff–sheriffs
For words ending in *y* with a vowel before it, add *s*.	day–days, monkey–monkeys
For words ending in *o* with a consonant before it, usually add *es*; add *s* if the word relates to music.	radio–radios, piano–pianos, potato–potatoes
For words ending in *ch*, *sh*, *s*, *x*, or *z* add *es* at the end.	bench–benches, lash–lashes, fox–foxes
For some words ending in *f* or *fe*, change *f* or *fe* to *v* and add *es*.	elf–elves, loaf–loaves, knife–knives, wolf–wolves
For words ending in *y* with a consonant before it, change *y* to *i* and add *es*.	lady–ladies
For some words, change the spelling of the singular form.	woman–women, child–children, goose–geese, mouse–mice
For some words, use the same form for both singular and plural.	sheep–sheep, deer–deer

Always be sure to check a dictionary if you are not sure about the correct spelling of a word.

Directions Read the paragraph below. Follow the steps and answer the questions.

Last Saturday our family had a garage sale. People came to our house to look at things. We had everything from dinner plates to old radios. Some people bought lots of things. Others just wanted to look around and talk. Our neighbor bought a set of steak knifes for five dollars. Her husband look through boxs of old books. One young couple bought an old baby carriage. My dad helped everyone who had questions. He even sold a carving of three gooses to some ladys from out of town.

Check all regular plural words in your writing.

1. Look at the third sentence. Which words are plurals?

   _____

2. What letter was added to make these words plural?

   _____

3. Are these words spelled correctly? What kind of plurals are they?

   _____

Check all irregular plural words in your writing.

4. Look at the fourth sentence. What word is an irregular plural?

   _____

5. What is the singular form of this word?

_____

6. Look at the sixth sentence. What are the plural nouns in this sentence?

_____

7. Are both of these forms correct?

_____

8. Which word should be changed? How should it be spelled?

_____

Step 3

Proofread all plural words in your writing.

9. Which plurals should be corrected in this paragraph? Begin with the first sentence.

_____

10. What is the correct form of these plurals?

_____

Ideas to Remember

> **regular plurals**—plurals that are formed by adding an *s* or *es* to the singular form of a noun
>
> **irregular plurals**—plurals that are formed by changing the form and spelling of the singular noun; example—*leaf–leaves*

Apply the New Jersey CPIs

Directions   Read each sentence. Decide which plural in parentheses is correct. Draw a circle around the correct word.

11. We thought that noise in the kitchen could be (meeses, mice).

12. I like (tomatoes, tomatos) in my salad.

13. Dad put new (shelfs, shelves) in my room.

14. Bring two new (pencils, penciles) to class tomorrow.

15. Grandpa caught four (fish, fishes) at the lake.

16. April put all her (dolles, dolls) on her bed.

17. Two (deer, deers) came to drink in the pond.

18. The zoo built a new home for the (monkies, monkeys).

19. Banks keep their money in (saves, safes).

20. I got two (watchs, watches) for my birthday.

Writing to Explain—Narrative
Today you will do a writing assignment about the poem below,
"Too Busy." Read the poem and then read the writing prompt.

Too Busy
by Bruce Lansky

I've folded all my laundry
and put it in the drawer.
I've changed my linen, made my bed,
and swept my bedroom floor.

I've emptied out the garbage
and fixed tomorrow's lunch.
I've baked some cookies for dessert
and given Dad a munch.

I've searched the house for pencils
and sharpened every one.
There are so many things to do
when homework must be done.

Writing to Entertain—Narrative

What is the poet describing? Have you ever felt this way? Describe a time when you felt like you had too much to do. Think about the following questions before you write your answer.

- **Do you have daily chores to do at home?**
- **Are you always able to get them all done?**
- **Was there ever a time when you were not able to get them all done?**
- **What have you done to organize all your jobs, including schoolwork?**

You may take notes, create a web, or do other prewriting work. Then write your narrative. Use your own paper or write in your literary response journal.

Here is a checklist for you to follow to help you do your best writing. Before you begin writing, read the checklist silently. Reread it as often as you need.

Writer's Checklist

Remember to:

- ❏ Keep the central idea or topic in mind.
- ❏ Keep your audience in mind.
- ❏ Support your ideas with details, explanations, and examples.
- ❏ State your ideas in a clear sequence.
- ❏ Include an opening and a closing.
- ❏ Use a variety of words and vary your sentence structure.
- ❏ State your opinion or conclusion clearly.
- ❏ Capitalize, spell, and use punctuation correctly.
- ❏ Write neatly.

After you write your composition, read what you have written. Use the checklist to make certain that your writing is the best it can be.

Focus on the New Jersey CCCS

Think about times that you agree or disagree with your friends. What does *agree* mean? If a subject and verb agree in a sentence, what does that mean?

Guided Instruction

What else should be checked as you edit your writing? An important problem to look for is **subject-verb agreement**. The subject of a sentence can be **singular**, or one. If it is, then the verb must also be singular. A singular present tense verb usually ends in *s*.

- **Joe rides** his bicycle every day.

The subject of a sentence can be **plural**, or more than one. If it is, then the verb must also be plural. A plural present tense verb usually does not end in *s*.

- **The children ride** their bicycles every day.

A sentence is incorrect if the subject and verb don't agree. A singular subject cannot have a plural verb.

- **Joe ride** his bicycle every day.

Sometimes two subjects are connected by *and*. Two subjects connected by *and* in a sentence always take a plural verb.

- **My mother and my father ride** bicycles, too.

Directions Read the following sentences. Look at the word choices in parentheses. Think about the correct word choice for each sentence. Follow the steps. Answer the questions.

1. My mother (bake, bakes) a cake on my birthday.

2. Jim and Dustin (need, needs) to eat dinner.

3. My classmates (play, plays) soccer at recess.

4. The man (want, wants) to buy a car.

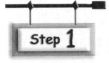

Step 1

Use a singular verb with a singular subject.

1. What is subject-verb agreement?

   _____

   _____

2. Look at the first sentence. What is the subject?

   _____

3. Is the subject singular or plural?

   _____

4. Look at the verb choices. Which verb is correct?

   _____

5. Another sentence has a singular subject. Write this sentence with the correct verb.

   _____

Step 2

Use a plural verb with a plural subject.

6. Look at the third sentence. What is the subject?

_____

7. Is the subject singular or plural?

_____

8. Look at the verb choices. Which verb is correct?

_____

Step 3

Use a plural verb with two subjects connected by the word *and.*

9. Look at the second sentence. What are the two subjects?

_____

10. Which verb is correct for this sentence?

_____

Ideas to Remember

subject-verb agreement—a subject and verb agree when both are singular or both are plural

**Apply the
New Jersey
CPIs**

Directions Read the sentences. Look at the verb choices in parentheses.
Circle the correct verb so that there is subject-verb agreement.

11. Mrs. Brown (plan, plans) to go shopping.

12. The boys (ride, rides) their skateboards after school.

13. The baby (spill, spills) juice during breakfast.

14. Police officers (help, helps) find lost children.

15. Some teachers (grade, grades) papers every day.

16. My sister and brother (love, loves) pizza.

17. Amy (take, takes) piano lessons.

18. They (like, likes) that movie.

19. She (score, scores) a goal for the team.

20. Our school (close, closes) during bad snowstorms.

Writing to Inform—Report

NJ ASK Practice

Your science teacher has asked you to write a report about the strangest weather you ever experienced. Tell about the weather and what happened around you because of it. Think about the following points.

- **What was the weather like?**
- **What caused the weather to happen?**
- **What did people do because of the weather?**
- **Did the weather cause damage to trees or buildings? How?**
- **How did you feel during the time the weather happened?**
- **Were there lasting problems because of the weather? What were they?**

You may take notes, create a web, or do other prewriting work. Then write your narrative. Use your own paper or write in your literary response journal.

Here is a checklist for you to follow to help you do your best writing. Before you begin writing, read the checklist silently as it is read to you. Reread it as often as you need.

Writer's Checklist

Remember to:

❑ Keep the central idea or topic in mind.

❑ Keep your audience in mind.

❑ Support your ideas with details, explanations, and examples.

❑ State your ideas in a clear sequence.

❑ Include an opening and a closing.

❑ Use a variety of words and vary your sentence structure.

❑ State your opinion or conclusion clearly.

❑ Capitalize, spell, and use punctuation correctly.

❑ Write neatly.

After you write your composition, read what you have written. Use the checklist to make certain that your writing is the best it can be.

Focus on the New Jersey CCCS

Have you ever tried to ride a bicycle after the chain falls off? What happens to it? How can sentences be like bicycles? What happens if all the parts of a sentence don't work together? Why do all the parts of a sentence have to fit together for a reader to understand it?

Guided Instruction

The parts of a sentence are called **parts of speech**. Some important parts of speech are **nouns**, **verbs**, and **pronouns**. Another important part of speech is a **conjunction**. Read about what each part of speech does.

Nouns name people, places, or things. Some examples of nouns are:

Margaret, Toronto, diskette

Verbs tell what nouns do. Sometimes they show action. Sometimes they show being. Some examples of verbs are:

Action: *run, throw, write, sit, read*
Being: *am, is*

Pronouns take the place of nouns. We use pronouns to keep from using the same nouns again and again. Some examples of pronouns are:

he, she, her, him, it, they, them

Conjunctions are words that join, or connect, ideas, or parts of sentences together. Some examples of conjunctions are:

and, but, or

Directions Listen as your teacher models this activity. Read the sentences below. Follow the steps. Answer the questions.

A. Molly and Sean walked to the beach.

B. They played in the water or the sand.

C. She built sand castles.

D. He ran into the waves.

E. Now they are both sunburned.

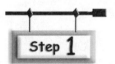

Find the nouns in your work.

1. What nouns are in Sentence A?

   _____

2. Which sentence has no nouns?

   _____

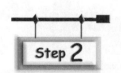

Find the pronouns in your work.

3. Which sentences have pronouns?

   _____

4. Which pronoun takes the place of *Molly?*

   _____

5. Which pronoun takes the place of *Sean?*

   _____

6. Which pronoun takes the place of both *Molly* and *Sean?*

   _____

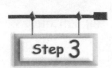

Step 3

Find the verbs in
your work.

7. Which verbs show action in these sentences?

_____

8. Which verb shows being in these sentences?

_____

Step 4

Find the
conjunctions in
your work.

9. Which sentences have conjunctions? What are they?

_____

 Ideas to Remember

noun—names people, places, or things
verb—tells what nouns do. Sometimes they show action.
    Sometimes they show being
pronoun—takes the place of a noun
conjunctions—words that join, or connect, ideas, or parts
    of sentences together

Directions Read each sentence. Then read the words in parentheses.
Decide which word best fits in the sentence. Circle the word you choose.

10. Mary Rose got a new (it, kitten) for her birthday.

11. The kitten will be a good pet for (her, and).

12. (Him, She) named the kitten Prince.

13. The kitten (likes, is) to play with a ball of string.

14. Both her Mom (his, and) Dad like to play with the kitten, too.

15. (It, Or) likes to sleep on Mary Rose's bed.

16. Mary Rose puts (it, she) on her lap when she reads.

17. The kitten (has, purrs) loudly on Mary Rose's lap.

18. Prince is happy with (him, his) new home.

19. He will grow up to be a fine (cat, it).

20. (Her, She) thinks about (her, she) cat all day.

**NJ ASK
Practice**

Writing to Explain—Narrative

Using the picture as a guide, write a story about what might be happening and what might happen next.

You may take notes, create a web, or do other prewriting work. Then write your narrative. Use your own paper or write in your literary response journal.

Here is a checklist for you to follow to help you do your best writing. Before you begin writing, read the checklist silently. Reread it as often as you need.

Writer's Checklist

Remember to:

❏ Keep the central idea or topic in mind.

❏ Keep your audience in mind.

❏ Support your ideas with details, explanations, and examples.

❏ State your ideas in a clear sequence.

❏ Include an opening and a closing.

❏ Use a variety of words and vary your sentence structure.

❏ State your opinion or conclusion clearly.

❏ Capitalize, spell, and use punctuation correctly.

❏ Write neatly.

After you write your composition, read what you have written. Use the checklist to make certain that your writing is the best it can be.

Focus on the New Jersey CCCS

What do you think about when you write? Do you think about who will read your work? Do you write things for your friends to read? Is all your writing just for your teacher to read? How will you share your work with your audience?

Guided Instruction

You have finished your writing. Now you can **publish** it. When you publish writing, you put it in a form share it with an audience. There are many different ways to share your work. To choose a way, ask yourself:

- Who did I write this for?

- How can I reach this audience?

Then decide which form of publishing you will use. You could publish your writing as a **letter**, **article**, **report**, **booklet**, or **poster**.

Here are some ideas for sharing your writing:

- Make a class magazine, book, or newspaper of your work and your classmates' work.

- Frame it on colored construction paper and hang it on a bulletin board.

- Send it to a magazine that publishes student work.

- Make copies of it for your friends and family.

- Post it on the Internet.

- Make a poster and hang it on a school wall.

Directions Use the prewriting steps below to help you decide and organize.

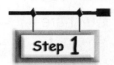

Think about the best audience for your writing.

1. Who is the best audience for a report about how to be a goaltender—a group of musicians magazine or a soccer team?

   _____

2. Who is the best audience for a report about mountain trails—a cooking class or a hiking club?

   _____

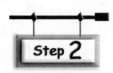

Think about how to reach an audience.

3. You've written an article about school safety rules. Which would be the best place to publish this article—your city newspaper or your school newsletter?

   _____

4. Why did you choose this answer?

   _____

   _____

   _____

Think about the best form for your writing.

5. You could publish your writing as a letter, article, report, booklet, or poster. Which form would you use for an illustrated report on different kinds of seashells? Why?

   _____

   _____

 **Ideas to Remember**

publish—to put your writing in a form where an audience can read it

forms of publishing—the different forms you can use for your writing; examples are a letter, an article, a report, a booklet, or a poster

 **Apply the New Jersey CPIs**

Directions Read each writing assignment. Choose the best audience for each. Then choose the best form of publishing. Fill in the circle beside each answer you choose.

6. Who is the best audience for a report about how to take care of a cat?

   Ⓐ a music club

   Ⓑ a biking club

   Ⓒ people who own cats

   Ⓓ a stamp collecting club

   What is the best form of publishing for this report?

   Ⓐ an article in a magazine for cat owners

   Ⓑ a booklet kept in the school office

   Ⓒ a note on a classroom bulletin board

   Ⓓ a long novel to be sold in book stores

7. Who is the best audience for an explanation of what shoes are best for running?

    Ⓐ   students who don't study well

    Ⓑ   students who try out for the relay team

    Ⓒ   students who want to form a chess club

    Ⓓ   students who are in the choir

What is the best form of publishing for this explanation?

    Ⓐ   a letter written to your favorite relative

    Ⓑ   an information sheet posted in the gym

    Ⓒ   a booklet to be kept in the school library

    Ⓓ   a flyer to be handed out at a baseball game

8. Who is the best audience for a review of the latest children's books?

    Ⓐ   a group of pet owners

    Ⓑ   a gardening club

    Ⓒ   a skateboarding club

    Ⓓ   students in your school

What is the best form of publishing for this review?

    Ⓐ   a booklet to be kept in the school library

    Ⓑ   an article in a national music magazine

    Ⓒ   a bulletin board at the supermarket

    Ⓓ   an information sheet for the principal's office

Writing to Explain—Narrative

NJ ASK Practice

Think about the kinds of things that are published. Think about some of the things you read every day. Are all these things published? Think about these questions as you write.

- **What forms of published writing do you read?**
- **What kinds of published writing do you like?**
- **What kinds of published writing do you not like?**
- **What kinds of published writing would you like to read more of?**
- **Where do you find these published writing pieces?**

You may take notes, create a web, or do other prewriting work. Then write your narrative. Use your own paper or write in your literary response journal.

Here is a checklist for you to follow to help you do your best writing. Before you begin writing, read the checklist silently as it is read to you. Reread it as often as you need.

Writer's Checklist

Remember to:

❏ Keep the central idea or topic in mind.

❏ Keep your audience in mind.

❏ Support your ideas with details, explanations, and examples.

❏ State your ideas in a clear sequence.

❏ Include an opening and a closing.

❏ Use a variety of words and vary your sentence structure.

❏ State your opinion or conclusion clearly.

❏ Capitalize, spell, and use punctuation correctly.

❏ Write neatly.

After you write your composition, read what you have written. Use the checklist to make certain that your writing is the best it can be.

**Focus
on the
New Jersey
CCCS**

You may want to know how graders will grade your writing when you take the *New Jersey Assessment of Skills and Knowledge*. This lesson will show you some of the **writing mechanics**, or things that make up good writing, that graders look for when they read your writing.

**Guided
Instruction**

The state of New Jersey has written a rubric. A **rubric** is a list of things graders look for to help them decide how well you write. The rubric is made up of four parts. They are: *Content and Organization*, *Usage*, *Sentence Construction*, and *Mechanics*. Now turn to page 291 and review the rubric. This is just like the rubric graders will use to evaluate your writing.

Now that you have seen the rubric, read the following information to see what graders look for in your writing.

Directions Follow the steps and read each paragraph.

**Content and
Organization**

Graders check to see if you have written an **opening** and a **closing** for your writing. They watch to see if you write about only one **topic**. They want to know if your ideas about your topic go together. They check to see if your main ideas are supported by **examples** and **details**. Graders check to see if one idea leads to another and that your ideas don't skip around and confuse the reader. They want to know that you have done your best writing. They also check to see if your details work with the **main ideas** and that you have used different **supporting details**. Good writing doesn't use the same details over and over.

Word Usage

Graders check to see if your subjects and verbs **agree** in number. They look for **singular subjects** with **singular verbs**, and **plural subjects** with **plural verbs**. Graders look to see how well you use **pronouns**. When you use past, present, and future verbs, make sure you use them correctly. Graders also look to see whether you have used different words to say exactly what you mean. If you use **adjectives**, or words to describe nouns or verbs, be sure that you have used ones that say exactly what you mean.

Sentence Construction and Mechanics

Graders want to know that you have written different kinds of sentences. Don't use only **statements**, or **declarative** sentences, to write your essay. Be sure that each sentence has a **subject** and a **verb**. Be sure that when you change main ideas you also change paragraphs. Remember to **indent** each paragraph to signal that you have made a change.

Graders will also check your writing mechanics. So, make sure that all of your words are **spelled** correctly, especially the more difficult words that give you the most trouble. They also look for correct use of **capitalization** and **punctuation**.

Ideas to Remember

writing mechanics—things that make up good writing, that graders look for when they read your writing

rubric—a list of things for graders to look for to help them decide how well you write

adjectives—words to describe nouns or verbs

**Apply the
New Jersey
CPIs**

Directions Read each question below and answer it on the lines provided.

1. Why do graders check to see how well you organized your thoughts and ideas in your writing?

_____

_____

_____

2. Why is it necessary to use supporting details with your main ideas?

_____

_____

3. Why should you have an opening and a closing to your essay?

    _____

    _____

4. Why is it important that subjects and verbs agree in
    number? Why are correct pronouns necessary? Why is it
    important that you have good usage when you write?

    _____

    _____

    _____

5. Why would graders look for good use of mechanics?

    _____

    _____

    _____

Writing to Inform—Report

NJ ASK Practice

People plant trees, bushes, and flowers. They can make an area beautiful. What could be planted in your yard or in your neighborhood to make your area beautiful? Write a report describing your plan. Before you write, think about the following points.

- **What area near your home could be made more beautiful?**
- **Why do trees, bushes, and flowers make an area more beautiful?**
- **What things would you like to plant in your area?**
- **How can you explain your plan to a friend.**

You may take notes, create a web, or do other prewriting work. Then write your report. Use your own paper or write in your literary response journal.

Here is a checklist for you to follow to help you do your best writing. Before you begin writing, read the checklist silently. Reread it as often as you need.

Writer's Checklist

Remember to:

❏ Keep the central idea or topic in mind.

❏ Keep your audience in mind.

❏ Support your ideas with details, explanations, and examples.

❏ State your ideas in a clear sequence.

❏ Include an opening and a closing.

❏ Use a variety of words and vary your sentence structure.

❏ State your opinion or conclusion clearly.

❏ Capitalize, spell, and use punctuation correctly.

❏ Write neatly.

After you write your composition, read what you have written. Use the checklist to make certain that your writing is the best it can be.

NJ ASK Practice

Writing to Explain—Article

Use this picture as a guide. Write a story about what might be happening in this picture. Tell what might happen next.

You may take notes, create a web, or do other prewriting work. Then, write your story. Use your own paper or write in your literary response journal. Here is a checklist for you to follow to help you do your best writing. Before you begin writing, read the checklist silently as it is read to you. Reread it as often as you need.

Writer's Checklist

Remember to:

❒ Keep the central idea or topic in mind.

❒ Keep your audience in mind.

❒ Support your ideas with details, explanations, and examples.

❒ Write the events of the story in a clear sequence.

❒ Include an opening and a strong ending.

❒ Use a variety of words and vary your sentence structure.

❒ Capitalize, spell, and use punctuation correctly.

❒ Write neatly.

After you write your composition, read what you have written. Use the checklist to make certain that your writing is the best it can be.

Today you will do a writing assignment. The poem below, "A Captain's Cat," may give you ideas for your writing. Read the poem and then read the writing prompt.

A Captain's Cat
by Laurie Byro

A captain's cat,
he went to sea
and took good care of mice.
He sailed the fine ship *Cowardly*
and sang his cat's advice.

"Keep rats below, and gulls above,
and mind we keep them hearty.
Good eatin' they will always make
should they attend our party."

"Now cats are good for scrubbin' decks,
we have a scrubber's tongue —
we force sea dogs to walk the plank
unless their chores are done."

The captain had one fleshy leg,
the other made of oak.
He didn't like to show it off,
to plain landlubbin' folk.

But his first mate, the captain's cat,
still loved it just the same.
He used it as his scratchin' post
and sailed the Spanish Main.

Writing to Explain—Narrative

Imagine you have been asked by the school librarian to write a review of this poem. It will be used for other students' research. Your review should include your opinion with information from the poem to help you make your argument. Include the following:

- What do you think about this poem?
- Did you like it? Did you not like it?
- Have you ever read anything else by this writer?
- How will you try to persuade your audience? Should they read it? Or should they find something else?

You may take notes, create a web, or do other prewriting work. Then, write your story. Use your own paper or write in your literary response journal.

Here is a checklist for you to follow to help you do your best writing. Before you begin writing, read the checklist silently as it is read to you. Reread it as often as you need.

Writer's Checklist

Remember to:

❏ Keep the central idea or topic in mind.

❏ Keep your audience in mind.

❏ Support your ideas with details, explanations, and examples.

❏ State your ideas in a clear sequence.

❏ Include an opening and a closing.

❏ Use a variety of words and vary your sentence structure.

❏ State your opinion or conclusion clearly.

❏ Capitalize, spell, and use punctuation correctly.

❏ Write neatly.

After you write your composition, read what you have written. Use the checklist to make certain that your writing is the best it can be.

How is listening to a story different from reading it out loud? What makes listening to a story fun? What should you remember to do when you read aloud?

Directions Look at the picture below. Answer the questions that follow.

Guided Instruction

1. Who is speaking to the class? Draw a box around this pupil's head.

2. How many people are not paying attention to the speaker? Draw a circle around each one of them.

3. Draw a triangle around the pupil who is paying attention to the boy reading the story.

4. Why do you think some of the pupils are not paying attention?

_____

_____

_____

_____

Focus on the New Jersey CCCS

You are taking part in a class discussion. What should you remember when you are speaking during the discussion? What should you do when you are listening? How can you make sure that other people in the discussion listen to your ideas?

Guided Instruction

Speaking and listening skills are important in school and at home. What kinds of speaking presentations do you make in school? Some examples are:

- a speech you make to a club, class, or group;
- a story you read aloud;
- comments you make during a class discussion.

What kinds of speaking presentations do you listen to almost every day? Some examples are:

- announcements by the principal or your teacher;
- stories your friends tell you;
- a speech by a guest speaker in school;
- a radio or TV program or advertisement;
- a movie or video;
- a talk in your science, math, or social studies class;
- a site on the Internet that includes sound as well as text and pictures.

Keep these rules in mind as you make speeches or take part in discussions. Think about the rules as you listen to speaking presentations, too.

Pay Attention

When you are part of the audience, focus on the person who is speaking. Look directly at the speaker. Don't let your eyes drift around the room. Don't let anything distract you. If your mind starts to wander, try to redirect your focus.

Think About What You Will Say

When it is your turn to speak, state your **main idea** or point clearly. Have a clear purpose in mind. Use details to support your ideas. You might even compare your ideas with ones other people have already presented. Sum up your idea in order to conclude what you have to say.

Think About What You Hear

Think about the meaning of the words. Think about the ideas in a story, set of directions, poem, movie, TV show, or speech. Don't let the words "go in one ear and out the other." Ask yourself what the most important idea is. Think about what **details support** this idea. Connect any new ideas to information you have already learned or know about.

Take Notes

Write down notes. Write **key words** and list important names to remember. When you hear an important idea, write it down. Write details that go with each idea. Taking notes and **summarizing** will help you remember what you hear. You can use your notes to help plan your own comments.

Be Courteous

Listen carefully and respectfully as people speak or present programs. Take turns asking questions. Allow enough time for others to answer each question or ask their own questions. Take turns sharing your opinions. You will get new ideas as others talk, so listen carefully and take notes as ideas are shared.

Directions Read the steps. Then answer the questions.

Suppose that Earth Day is this Saturday. You want to lead a class discussion about Earth Day. You want to talk about how important it is to keep our world clean. You plan to ask your classmates to take part in a clean-up project. *You want their help cleaning up the school grounds on Saturday.* How do you choose what to say during the discussion?

Step 1

Decide on your purpose for holding the discussion.

Step 2

Think about the roles of the people taking part in the discussion.

1. Underline the sentence that tells what result you want from the discussion.

2. Circle the sentence that tells why the project is necessary.

3. Who will be taking part in the discussion?

4. What will the participants do when they are speaking?

   _____

   _____

5. What should the participants do when they are listening?

   _____

   _____

 Measuring Up® to the NJ Core Curriculum Content Standards

Step 3

Plan a way to get your audience to pay attention.

6. How can a speaker grab the audience's attention? Fill in the letter of the sentence that would be the best one to use at the beginning of your comments.

Ⓐ The soccer game is on Saturday.

Ⓑ It's important to protect our world.

Ⓒ Bring lots of trash bags with you.

Ⓓ The exercise will be good for you.

(Ideas to Remember)

audience—the people who will listen to a speech or watch television, movies, and shows

purpose—the reason for doing something

Apply the New Jersey CPIs

Directions Read along as your teacher reads this announcement aloud. Take notes of the important ideas you hear. Write your notes on the Persuasive Graphic Organizer shown on the next page.

We need volunteers to help with the soccer team picnic. We need help carrying boxes of food. There will be juice, sandwiches, fruit, and four kinds of cookies. Lots of tables and chairs also need to be set up. We're expecting more than 75 players and their families. Everything must be cleaned up after lunch. Please sign the sheet that will be passed around. Everyone needs to take a turn in helping with this project. That way we can have other activities throughout the year.

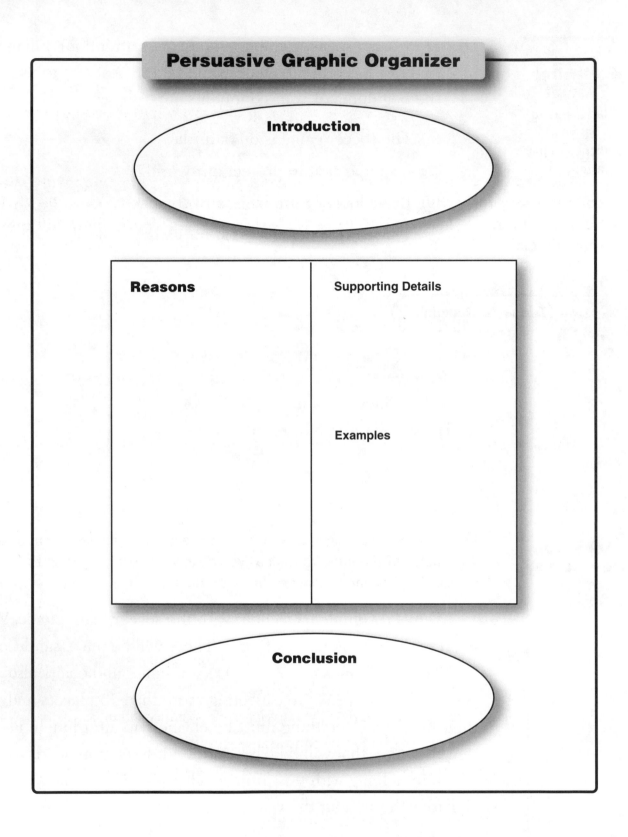

Persuasive Graphic Organizer

Introduction

Reasons | Supporting Details

Examples

Conclusion

Speaking Prompt

Pick Up Your Mess

Directions: Read the following to learn about the topic of your speech.

Situation

You are the cafeteria monitor for this week. Pupils in your class have been spilling more food than usual. The cafeteria floor has been a mess. Pupils haven't been cleaning up their spilled food. Yesterday it caused one boy to fall and hurt his arm.

Before You Present

Prepare a two-minute presentation for your classmates about the food problem. Include in your talk:

- why everyone should be careful not to spill food in the cafeteria.
- if they do spill food, clean it up.

Here is a checklist for you to follow to help you do your best speaking. Before you begin preparing your speech, read the checklist carefully. Reread it as often as you need. Use the checklist to make certain that your speaking is the best it can be.

Speaker's Checklist

When you speak, remember to:

☐ support your ideas with details, explanations, and examples.

☐ state your ideas in a clear order, or sequence.

☐ include an opening and a closing.

☐ use a variety of words and vary your sentence structure.

☐ state your opinion or conclusion clearly.

☐ speak clearly and slowly so your audience can hear what you say.

☐ show an interest in your topic.

☐ look up at your audience as much as possible.

**Focus
on the
New Jersey
CCCS**

What kinds of questions do you answer in your science, math, and reading classes? How are questions in different subjects alike? How are they different? Explain how answering questions helps you learn facts and ideas about important subjects and do well on tests.

**Guided
Instruction**

Try to be an **active listener**. As you listen to speeches and other speaking presentations, get involved. Think about what the speaker is saying. Ask yourself questions about the information. **Questioning** will help you pay close attention to what you hear. Listen for details that answer your questions.

Ask yourself some of the following questions:

- What is the topic of the presentation?
- What do I already know about the topic?
- What other information do I want to find out about the topic?
- What new ideas have I learned during the presentation?

You can organize your questions and answers by using a **KWL Chart**. It is a chart with three columns. In the first column, you list what you already *Know*. In the second column, you write questions that ask what you *Want* to learn. In the last column you write what you have *Learned* to answer to the questions.

Directions Read the steps. Then answer the questions on the next page.

Alicia is writing a report for science class. She plans to watch a TV program about the African elephant. She is using a KWL Chart to help her follow the program. Read her work below.

KWL Chart

Topic ___the African elephant___

What I **Know**	What I **Want** to Learn	What I **Learned**
The African elephant is very powerful but also gentle. African elephants live together in families.	Where in Africa do African elephants live? How big is the African elephant? What do African elephants eat? If African elephants are in danger of dying out, why?	These animals live in the area south of Africa's Sahara desert. African elephants can weigh between five-and-one-half and seven tons. These animals eat green grass and the buds of trees and shrubs. African elephants are in danger. People are turning the wild areas where they live into cities and farms. They are also being killed for their ivory tusks.

_____
_____
_____

Begin by writing down the topic of the oral presentation.

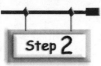

List some facts you already know about the topic.

List questions that will help you learn more about the topic.

1. Circle the topic of the TV program that Alicia is planning to watch.

2. What does Alicia already know about the African elephant?

_____

_____

3. What kinds of facts does Alicia want to learn about African elephants?

_____

_____

4. Think of another question Alicia could ask about African elephants. List your question in the second column of the chart.

_____

_____

5. Do you think Alicia is an active listener? Explain your answer.

_____

_____

6. What has Alicia learned about where elephants live in Africa?

Take notes during the oral presentation. Use your notes to help you answer the questions you have listed in your chart.

_____

_____

_____

 Ideas to Remember

active listener —a listener who pays close attention and asks himself or herself questions about the information being presented

questioning —preparing for an oral presentation; thinking about what you already know about the topic and writing questions to answer while listening to the presentation

Apply the New Jersey CPIs

Directions You have been given an assignment to make an oral report about a famous inventor or explorer. Choose a person you would like to talk about. Use the first column of the KWL Chart below to list facts you already know. In the middle column, write questions that you need to answer in order to plan your report. Use books from the school or public library, an encyclopedia, or the Internet to find answers to your questions. Write what you have learned from your research in the third column of the chart. Then answer the questions on the next page.

KWL Chart

Topic _____

What I **Know**	What I **Want** to Learn	What I **Learned**

_____

_____

_____

1. What would be a main idea you would want to include in your report?

    _____

    _____

    _____

2. Write an opening sentence for your report that might grab the audience's attention.

    _____

    _____

    _____

3. List several facts you plan to include in your report.

    _____

    _____

    _____

4. Write a sentence that you might use to close your report.

    _____

    _____

    _____

Who Is Better—Animated Characters or Real Actors?

Speaking Prompt

Directions: Read the following to learn about the topic of your speech.

Situation

In some movies, real people act out all the roles. Other movies feature animated or cartoon characters. These animation actors can be drawn by hand or on a computer. A few movies have even combined animation and real actors. Some real people take parts. Other parts are animated characters.

Today, you are going to give your opinion on which type of actors you prefer to watch: real people or animated characters. Be sure to present reasons and examples to support your opinion.

Before You Present

Prepare a two-minute presentation for your classmates about the kind of movie character you like best. Include in your talk:

- the titles of one or more movies that you like a lot.
- why you prefer movies that feature animated characters or real people in movies.

Here is a checklist for you to follow to help you do your best speaking. Before you begin preparing your speech, read the checklist carefully. Reread it as often as you need. Use the checklist to make certain that your speaking is the best it can be.

Speaker's Checklist

When you speak, remember to:

❒ keep the central idea or topic in mind.

❒ support your ideas with details, explanations, and examples.

❒ state your ideas in a clear sequence.

❒ include an opening and a closing

❒ use a variety of words and vary your sentence structure.

❒ state your opinion or conclusion clearly.

❒ speak clearly and slowly so your audience can hear what you say.

❒ show an interest in your topic.

❒ look up at your audience as much as possible

Focus on the New Jersey CCCS

How would you like to be in a circus? Would you rather clean the garage? Which activity seems fun? Why does the other one not seem fun? How do words present different feelings and moods?

Guided Instruction

If you are giving a good speech, your listeners will seem interested. Your speech is probably not going well if the audience is bored. The words you choose can improve the way you take part in oral presentations. Words that appeal to the senses affect listeners. If you say "cleaning the garage is a tiresome chore," your audience knows that you don't enjoy this job. When you say "it is a great challenge to clean the garage," listeners know you like to do hard tasks. Keep your main idea in mind. Choose words that fit your purpose.

Make lists of **adjectives**, or descriptive words. These might be words from stories or classroom discussions. You can even brainstorm with others while you prepare group speeches and presentations. Choose words that really affect your listeners. There are different purposes for speaking:

Persuade

This type of speaking and writing tries to affect listeners. The speaker will urge listeners to agree with the main idea. Use words that appeal to the listeners' feelings, such as *important, enjoyable, pleasing, scary, worrying*, and others.

Explain

Some speeches are presented to **describe** or explain facts and ideas. You might take part in a discussion about the need to keep oceans clean. Choose words that fit your topic, such as *recycling, protection*, and *antipollution*. These words will make your speech lively and interesting. They will also show how well you have studied your topic.

Seek Information

Group discussions help you find out new ideas and facts. You have learned how questioning helps you plan and write a speech. Questions can also help you take part in a discussion or even take part in an interview. Remember that the six basic questions, Who? What? When? Where? Why? and How? will help you ask all the necessary questions to find out what you need to know.

Directions Follow the steps and answer the questions.

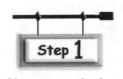

Step 1

Choose words that fit your topic.

1. New Jersey and its geography are being studied in your social studies class. You will take part in a discussion of the state's cities, rivers, and ocean. What words fit the topic of the discussion? Fill in the letters of the words that you choose.

   Ⓐ ocean

   Ⓑ mountains

   Ⓒ deserts

   Ⓓ palm trees

2. Open house will be held on Friday. You need help decorating the school. You are asking for volunteers to stay after school. The following sentence might be from your speech. Circle the word that is overused.

   We have a pretty school, but we must make pretty decorations by Friday so our parents can see that we worked pretty hard, too.

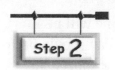

Step 2

Choose words that affect listeners.

3. You want the class to join you in working on the decorations. In the speech, you talk about how much everyone should care about the school. Which pair of the synonyms could be used to replace the last two overused words from question 2? Fill in the letter of the answer you choose.

Ⓐ good, incredibly

Ⓑ nice, somewhat

Ⓒ clean, gorgeous

Ⓓ beautiful, very

Ideas to Remember

> **word choice**—choosing words that are fresh and precise to replace common, weak words; or choosing words that fit a particular topic

Apply the New Jersey CPIs

Directions You will take part in a group discussion. The topic will be homework. Some people feel that the last part of the school day should be free time when homework can be done. Other people want time for sports and spending time with friends. Choose one of these ideas. Plan what you will say in the discussion. Write your ideas on the chart shown below.

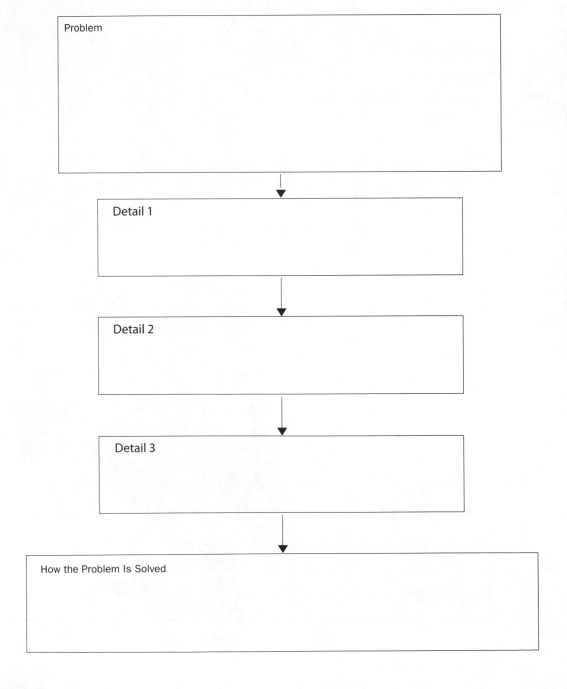

Graphic Organizer
Problem/Solution Chart

Problem

Detail 1

Detail 2

Detail 3

How the Problem Is Solved

Speaking Prompt

Directions: Read the following to learn about the topic of your speech.

Situation

Imagine you live in the United States in the late 1700s. You have been traveling with your family as part of a wagon train. You want to find a good place to live. You think you have found the perfect place. It is located along a wide river. It has good soil in which to grow crops. No other people live there now. It has many animals to hunt.

Today, you are going to talk to the rest of the class about the place you have chosen.

Before You Present

Prepare a two-minute presentation for your classmates about why you have chosen to live in this place. Present the speech to convince them to live there with you. Include in your talk:

- why you think it is a good place to live.
- why the pupils in the class should live there too.

Here is a checklist for you to follow to help you do your best speaking. Before you begin preparing your speech, read the checklist carefully. Reread it as often as you need. Use the checklist to make certain that your speaking is the best it can be.

Speaker's Checklist

When you speak, remember to:

❏ keep the central idea or topic in mind.

❏ support your ideas with details, explanations, and examples.

❏ state your ideas in a clear sequence.

❏ include an opening and a closing.

❏ use a variety of words and vary your sentence structure.

❏ state your opinion or conclusion clearly.

❏ speak clearly and slowly so your audience can hear what you say.

❏ show an interest in your topic.

❏ look up at your audience as much as possible.

Focus on the New Jersey CCCS

Imagine that you are making a speech or reading something out loud today. You must write your speech or choose something to read. How do you get ready to make your oral presentation?

Guided Instruction

Now you have finished writing your speech. You may have chosen a selection to read. You might even be part of a group that will be putting on a skit. Your speech is written on several notecards. You have a copy of the selection you will read aloud. You have taken a part to play in the skit. What things do you need to check? You can use a **checklist**.

Step 1

Check your notes.

Directions Read the steps. Then answer the questions.

Check these things:

- Are there words that are hard to pronounce? Practice saying them until you get them right.
- Are the notes easy to read?
- Are the notes in the right order?
- Is the selection printed so that it will be easy to read?
- What feelings will you have to present while playing a particular character?

1. Where do you look to find out how to pronounce unfamiliar words?

_____

2. Why should a speech show your personal feelings, too?

_____

_____

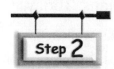

Step 2

Check pictures, charts, or music.

Check these things:

● Are you using pictures? Are they in order?

● Are you using a chart? Is it easy to read?

● Are you playing music? Is the player ready to go?

3. When should you use pictures and charts?

_____

_____

_____

Step 3

Practice giving your speech or reading aloud.

Check these things:

● Is your voice loud enough?

● Are you speaking or reading clearly?

● Are you speaking at the right speed? (Don't go too fast.)

4. How should you stand when you make a speech?

_____

_____

Ideas to Remember

checklist—a list of things to check before doing a task or project

Apply the New Jersey CPIs

Directions Follow along as your teacher reads the paragraph below. Imagine that you are preparing to read this selection out loud. Then answer the questions.

Igor Stravinsky was one of Russia's greatest musicians. Today, his music is thought to be among the world's best. This was not always the case, however. He wrote the music for the ballet "The Rite of Spring." This ballet was first staged in Paris in 1913. Stravinsky's music was very different from the music of the past. Most of the audience hated it. They began throwing things at the stage. Fights broke out all over the theater. Finally, the police had to be brought in. People today love Stravinsky's music. If your city or state has a ballet company, it has probably done its own presentation of "The Rite of Spring."

1. What books can you use to check the pronunciations and spellings of the Russian name and other words in the selection?

   _____

2. Where can you find rules to follow for grammar and punctuation?

   _____

3. What sources can you use to check the facts included in this selection?

   _____

   _____

   _____

4. How could you present your audience with the music for "The Rite of Spring"?

_____

_____

_____

5. At what point in the speech should the musical presentation be made? What tools will be necessary?

_____

_____

_____

6. If possible, where should you practice your presentation of this selection? Why?

_____

_____

_____

_____

Listening Practice

Directions Read along as your teacher reads "A Snake Named Rover." As you listen, think about the details of the poem. Write your answers on the Narrative Poetry Map below. Then use your notes to answer the questions that follow the poem. Fill in the circle beside the answer that you choose for questions 1 through 5. Write answers to questions 6 and 7.

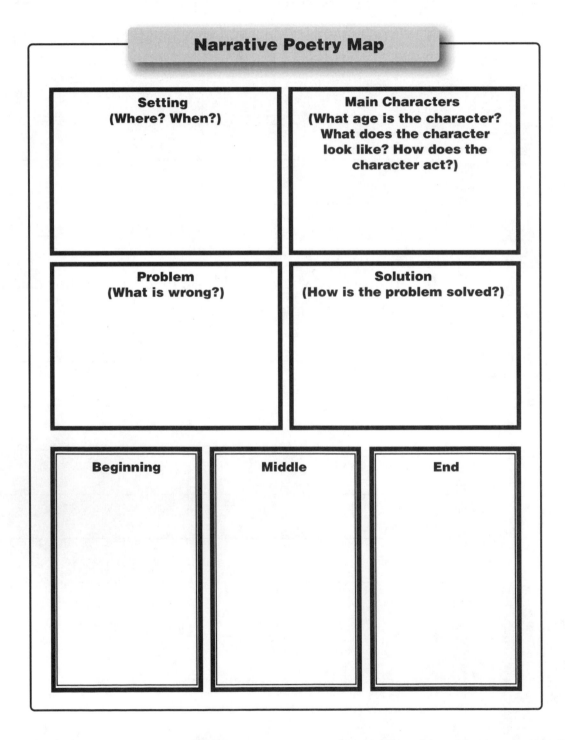

Narrative Poetry Map

Setting
(Where? When?)

Main Characters
(What age is the character? What does the character look like? How does the character act?)

Problem
(What is wrong?)

Solution
(How is the problem solved?)

Beginning

Middle

End

A Snake Named Rover
by Maxine Jeffris

Mom wouldn't let me have a dog
"With all the mess they make!"
So, if I couldn't have a dog,
I said I'd like a snake.

My mother gasped quite audibly,
But Dad approved the plan,
"A snake," he gulped, "a real live snake . . .
Well, sure, I guess you can."

We went to Ralph's Repulsive Pets
And bought a yard of asp.
It coiled inside a paper bag
Held firmly in my grasp.

I put him in a big glass tank
And dubbed my new pet Rover,
But all the fun of owning it
Was very quickly over.

For all he did was flick his tongue
Once or twice each minute,
While nervous Mom rechecked the tank
To make sure he was in it.

Then one fine day, we don't know how,
My Rover disappeared.
My father told me not to fret,
But Mom was mighty scared.

We searched the house from front to back
And gave the yard a sweep.
By midnight we had given up
And tried to get some sleep.

At three A.M. my dad arose
To answer nature's call.
I heard him scream, I heard him swear,
And then I heard him fall.

For Dad had found the wayward pet
I'd given up for dead
Curled up inside his slipper
Lying right beside his bed.

Now Rover's living back at Ralph's
With frogs, and newts, and guppies,
And now I have a dog named Spot–
She'll soon be having puppies.

1. How were Mom and Dad different?

Ⓐ Mom didn't like any kind of pet, but Dad loved snakes.

Ⓑ Mom checked the snake to see if it needed food, but Dad left it alone.

Ⓒ Mom didn't want to have a snake, but Dad didn't mind.

Ⓓ Mom was afraid the snake would hurt the dog, but Dad knew they would get along.

2. How long was the pet snake?

Ⓐ a few inches

Ⓑ a yard

Ⓒ a mile

Ⓓ a few feet

3. Why was this pet so disappointing?

Ⓐ Rover didn't like his new family.

Ⓑ Rover didn't do anything interesting.

Ⓒ No one could get Rover to dance.

Ⓓ All Rover ever did was beg for food.

4. What caused the family to get rid of Rover and buy a dog?

Ⓐ Rover got out of the tank and scared Dad.

Ⓑ Mom found out that snakes made her sneeze.

Ⓒ Dad scared the snake with his slippers.

Ⓓ Rover and Spot could not get along.

5. **What problem is the family facing at the end of the poem?**

    Ⓐ   Spot gets out and is hard to find.

    Ⓑ   Dad learns that dogs like to chew slippers.

    Ⓒ   Spot is going to have puppies that will need a lot of care.

    Ⓓ   Mom spends too much time taking care of Spot.

For the open-ended questions, remember to:
- **Focus your response on the question asked.**
- **Answer all parts of the question.**
- **Give a complete explanation.**
- **Use specific information from the directions.**

---

6. **Why is the pet store called Ralph's Repulsive Pets? Think about the meaning of the word repulsive— something that people hate or can't stand. Describe snakes and how people feel about them. Explain the feelings people may have when they enter this kind of pet store.**

   Use details from the poem to support your answer.

   _____

   _____

   _____

   _____

   _____

   _____

7. What is the moral, or the message, of this poem?
Think about the kind of pet the child wanted at the
beginning of the poem. Describe the way that Mom
changed her mind about having a dog. Explain how
the family will be affected by the ideas in the
last stanza.

Use details from the poem to support your answer.

_____

_____

_____

_____

_____

_____

_____

_____

Focus on the New Jersey CCCS

Have you ever heard a good speech? What did the speaker do during the speech to keep your attention? Have you ever watched the president make a speech on TV?

Guided Instruction

You have learned the different steps to take for creating an effective speech. You have written your speech and practiced reading it aloud. You have learned how to listen carefully and take notes while taking part in discussions. What things should you do when taking part in a **presentation?** What will it take to make your speech or presentation successful? What are graders looking for and how can you earn the best score?

The state of New Jersey has written a **rubric**. A rubric is a list of things that graders use to help them score your presentation. The rubric is broken down into 5 scores—4 points is the highest score you can get and 0 points is the lowest. Now turn to page 292 and review the Open-Ended Scoring Rubric for Reading, Listening, and Viewing. This is just like the rubric graders will use to evaluate your speech.

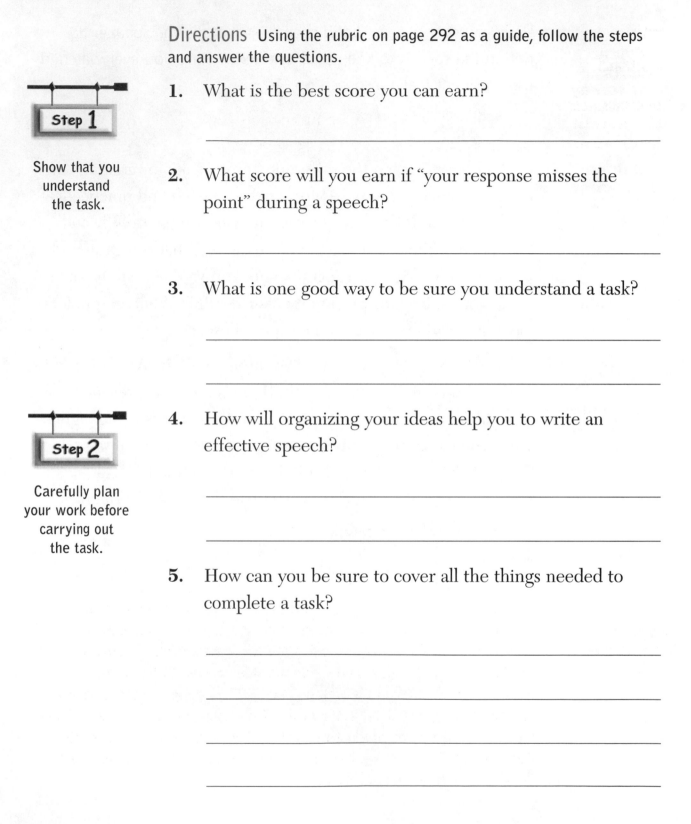

Directions Using the rubric on page 292 as a guide, follow the steps and answer the questions.

Step 1

Show that you understand the task.

1. What is the best score you can earn?

   _____

2. What score will you earn if "your response misses the point" during a speech?

   _____

3. What is one good way to be sure you understand a task?

   _____

   _____

Step 2

Carefully plan your work before carrying out the task.

4. How will organizing your ideas help you to write an effective speech?

   _____

   _____

5. How can you be sure to cover all the things needed to complete a task?

   _____

   _____

   _____

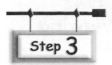

Step 3

Use details from the text in oral presentations.

6. What kind of explanation of the text will earn a score of 4 points?

7. What should you keep in mind as you read, speak, and listen?

_____

_____

_____

_____

Ideas to Remember

presentation—the act of giving a speech

rubric—a list of things for graders to look for to help them decide how well you write

Apply the New Jersey CPIs

Directions Work with a group and choose a speech or other oral presentation that you have already completed. Take turns making the presentation again. Make notes about each presentation by using the scoring chart on the next page. Use the Open-Ended Scoring Rubric for Reading, Listening, and Viewing on page 292 to study and score each presentation that is given in the group. Give each presenter a score. Then, give them a brief and productive explanation about why you scored the way you did. Do not make personal comments about a person, only tell about the features of each speech.

Assessment Guide for Reading, Listening, and Viewing

Scored by Pupil: _____ **OR Teacher:** _____

Read the pupil's paper. As you read, check the work with the points on the Scoring Rubric. Look at each row on the rubric. Find the set of facts that describes the work. Now, look at the top of the column for that set of facts. How many points are shown at the top of that column? Circle the number shown on the chart below. Write the number in the column titled "Total."

CATEGORY	NUMBER OF POINTS EARNED	TOTAL
Understanding of Task	0 1 2 3 4	
Areas that need work are:		
Completeness	0 1 2 3 4	
Areas that need work are:		
Expression of Explanation/Opinion	0 1 2 3 4	
Areas that need work are:		
	Total Number of Points	

While doing the next project it will be necessary to: _____

_____

_____

**Listening
Practice**

Directions Now read "Lucky Trade" on your own. As you read, think about the details of the poem. Write your answers on the Narrative Poetry Map below. Then use your notes to answer the questions that follow the poem.

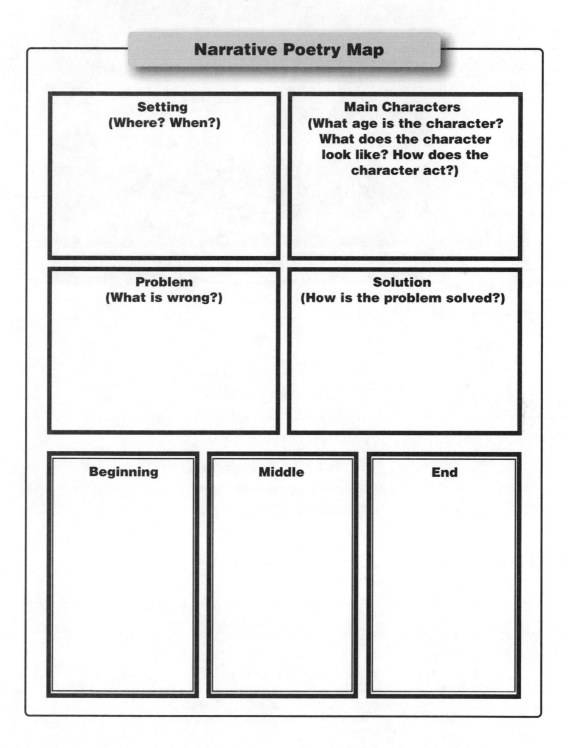

Narrative Poetry Map

**Setting
(Where? When?)**

**Main Characters
(What age is the character?
What does the character
look like? How does the
character act?)**

**Problem
(What is wrong?)**

**Solution
(How is the problem solved?)**

Beginning

Middle

End

Lucky Trade
by Matthew Fredericks

I told my mom I'd go to work
if she would go to school.
She thought that trading places once
just might be kind of cool.

So she agreed; I packed her lunch
and made her wash her face.
Then mother said, "I wonder why
you want to take my place?"

"I wonder what you do at work.
I'd like to meet your boss.
Now hurry up and brush your teeth
and don't forget to floss.

"There's just one other thing, Mom,
that I forgot to mention.
I'll pick you up at 4 o'clock
because today you have detention."

Listening Practice

1. **What is the setting of this poem?**

   Ⓐ morning at home

   Ⓑ evening at work

   Ⓒ afternoon at school

   Ⓓ nighttime at camp

2. **How does the child in the poem want to spend the day?**

   Ⓐ staying home to help around the house

   Ⓑ taking care of her mother who is sick

   Ⓒ helping her mother do home work

   Ⓓ taking her mother's place at work

3. **Why does the mother ask the question "I wonder why you want to take my place?"**

   Ⓐ She is puzzled by all the chores that have been done.

   Ⓑ She is not sure why her child wants to trade places.

   Ⓒ She fears that she will be late arriving at school.

   Ⓓ She wants to know why the child needs money.

4. **What will the child learn by taking her mother's place?**

   Ⓐ how her mother spends the money that she earns

   Ⓑ what her mother's job and boss are like

   Ⓒ what it's like eating breakfast alone every day

   Ⓓ why she looks so much like her mother

5. What trick is the child trying to pull?

- Ⓐ to keep her mother from knowing that she has detention
- Ⓑ a way of earning money for a brand-new bicycle to ride
- Ⓒ a new way to learn how to stay out of trouble
- Ⓓ to show how hard doing homework really is

For the open-ended questions, remember to:
- **Focus your response on the question asked.**
- **Answer all parts of the question.**
- **Give a complete explanation.**
- **Use specific information from the directions.**

---

6. What kind of person is the child in this poem? Think about the trick the child tries to pull. Describe the way that the child uses imagination. Explain the kinds of actions that may have led the child to get detention.

Use details from the poem to support your answer.

_____

_____

_____

_____

_____

_____

_____

7. What do you think will happen now that the mother knows the truth? Study the questions that the mother asks. Describe the way that people feel at being tricked. Explain how the mother might feel about her child having detention.

Use details from the poem to support your answer.

_____

_____

_____

_____

_____

_____

_____

Directions Today you will do a writing assignment. The picture below may give you ideas for your writing.

Writing to Speculate—Story

Who are the creatures in this picture? What have they been doing all day? Write a story describing the two characters. Explain what has happened to them. Include the following:

- **Tell who the two characters are.**
- **Describe the way they act towards each other.**
- **Is this a funny story? Is it serious?**
- **Is this a realistic story? Is it factual?**
- **Explain how they have affected each other's lives on this day.**
- **Describe the feelings each character experienced during the day's events.**

You may take notes, create a web, or do other prewriting work. Then, write your story. Use your own paper or write in your literary response journal.

Here is a checklist for you to follow to help you do your best writing. Before you begin writing, read the checklist. Reread it as often as you need.

Writer's Checklist

Remember to

- ❏ Keep the central idea or topic in mind.
- ❏ Keep your audience in mind.
- ❏ Support your ideas with details, explanations, and examples.
- ❏ State your ideas in a clear sequence.
- ❏ Include an opening and a closing.
- ❏ Use a variety of words and vary your sentence structure.
- ❏ State your opinion or conclusion clearly.
- ❏ Capitalize, spell, and use punctuation correctly.
- ❏ Write neatly.

After you write your article, read what you have written. Use the checklist to make certain that your writing is the best it can be.

Directions   Use details from the narrative selection to answer the following questions. Fill in the circle beside the answer that you choose.

From the Elephant Pit

A Tale from Tibet adapted by Elaine Lindy

A hunter once dug a pit to catch and trap wild elephants. One day, a man who was being chased by a lion fell into the pit, and then the lion followed a second later. Before they had time to pick themselves up, down came a mouse, closely followed by a snake who had been chasing it, and he, in turn, was followed by a falcon who had been trying to catch him.

So there they were—all five of them—caught in the elephant pit and unable to get out. Each as he picked himself up he tried to get away as far as possible from the others, for none knew what harm might come to him.

The man thought, "I must kill the lion or he will eat me."

The lion thought, "I must eat the man or he will kill me."

The falcon thought, "I must kill the snake or it may bite me."

The mouse thought, "Oh my! how I wish I could get away from all these big creatures!"

Thus they all sat silent, each one afraid to move lest some one or another pounce upon him and kill him.

In time the lion spoke: "Oh, honored ones," said he, "we are all comrades in misfortune. Let us promise not to hurt each other. Let each abide where he now is, while we plan a way to get out of this pit."

"Agreed!" cried all the others in haste, and especially pleased was the mouse.

Thus they all sat apart trying to think of a plan to escape, when the elephant hunter came to the pit.

"Why, what is all this?" the hunter cried, looking down.

"Oh, hunter, good hunter, kind hunter, please help us out!" cried the animals. "You see that we are not elephants."

"No, no, good hunter, I am not an elephant, I am not an elephant," squealed the mouse.

The hunter laughed. "No, you don't look much like an elephant, my little friend," he said. "I think I must help you all to escape."

The first animal that the hunter drew up was the lion. "Oh, hunter," said the lion, "I and the other animals will prove grateful to you and will help you for your kindness to us, so rescue them. But leave the man in the pit, for I warn you he will forget your kindness and do you harm."

The hunter, however, would not listen to the lion's advice, and rescued everyone.

A short time after this, the hunter fell ill of a great fever. He could not go into the woods to hunt for game, and he and his wife would have died but for the kindness of the lion. Every day the lion brought fresh meat and left it at the hunter's door.

One day while flying through the forest, the falcon saw something bright and glistening lying on the ground. He swooped down and found some beautiful gems. He carried the gems to the hunter's house and dropped them in his lap. Thus he, too, tried to repay the hunter for saving his life.

Now the gems found by the falcon belonged to the queen. She had lost them one day while passing through the wood. As she did not miss them until the next day, she thought they must have been stolen during the night, and told the king so.

The king at once sent out a man to find the gems, and the man he sent out was the very man who had fallen into the elephant pit and had been rescued by the hunter. In his search he came to the home of the sick hunter.

"Have you seen anything of such and such gems?" asked the man.

"Yes," answered the hunter, and brought them and spread them on the table.

"Where did you get these?" asked the man.

"The falcon whom I rescued from the pit brought them to me," said the hunter.

Now when the man looked on the gems, he craved them, and he said to the hunter, "These gems belong to the queen. She thinks someone has stolen them. I have been sent to find them. Unless I tell, nobody will ever know where they are. So, my friend, let us divide them. You keep half, and give half to me. Thus shall we both gain wealth and no one be the wiser."

"What!" cried the hunter. "Do you take me for a thief? No! No, I say! The gems shall be returned to our good queen."

"Then, my honest fellow," sneered the man, "you shall go to the palace as my prisoner."

He clapped his hands, and two soldiers rushed in. "Bind him and carry him to the king! It is he who has stolen the queen's jewels!"

The poor hunter, still weak from fever and illness, was carried bound to the palace. The king, believing the false man's story, would not listen to the poor hunter, but had him chained in a deep, dark dungeon.

The poor man was now in a pitiable state.

"Alas!" he said, "the lion spoke but the truth. "Because of the man that I rescued from my elephant pit I am now in this loathsome dungeon with none to pity me or to deliver me."

"Say not so, good friend," said the mouse, coming out of a corner. "I pity you, and it may be I who can deliver you. Keep up your courage. I will go now to find help."

The mouse ran off and soon returned with the snake. "Now I am glad," said the snake, "to have a chance to show my gratitude. Here is a little box of cream. Hide it in your chest. Today when the king walks in the garden, I will sting him on the heel. The cream in that little box alone can save his life. I urge you, use it."

True to his word, the snake bit the king as he walked in the garden.

"He will die! He will die!" wailed all the people. "None of our doctors know a cure for the bite of that snake."

As the queen sat weeping by the king's side, the mouse drew near and spoke to her. "O queen, there is one who can cure the king—the hunter who lies in the lowest dungeon. Send for him quickly, lest it be too late."

Hastily the queen gave the order, and the hunter was brought to the king's side. Taking the box of cream from his chest, he put some on the wound. At once the swelling went down, the pain disappeared, and the king was well again.

"What reward shall I give you?" said the king. "Ask what you will, my deliverer."

"O king," replied the hunter, "I ask only of you one great favor, that you listen to my story."

He then told the king the whole story. When he had ended, the king said, "The lion was right. Would that you had left the ungrateful man in the pit. Ho, soldiers, bring him to me and I will see that he is fitly punished."

But though the soldiers searched everywhere for the man, they could not find him. "I am glad he has escaped," said the hunter, "for I like not to see anybody suffer."

"Good," said the king, "it is noble thus to forgive an enemy. And now, my friend, I have need of a brave man like you in my palace. You shall live here as my chief hunter."

Thus, through the gratitude of the beasts, the hunter rose to high position and honor in the court of his king.

1. What does the man hope to catch in the pit he dug?

(A) lion

(B) elephant

(C) mouse

(D) snake

2. Which of the following does NOT fall into the pit?

(A) mouse

(B) falcon

(C) man

(D) elephant

3. What do the man and the animals promise to do if the hunter helps them out of the pit?

(A) to bring food to the hunter every day

(B) to stop fighting among themselves

(C) to help the hunter for getting them out of the pit

(D) to catch an elephant for the hunter

4. Which word BEST describes the hunter?

(A) sick

(B) caring

(C) worried

(D) funny

5. What is another good title for this story?

(A) The Importance of Being Honest

(B) How to Become Rich

(C) When to Do What You Want to Do

(D) Why Animals Talk

6. What lesson did you learn from this story?

- Explain how the characters were alike and how they were different.

- Describe how each character ended up.

- Tell what you think will happen next in the man's life.

Use details from the story to support your answer.

_____

_____

_____

_____

_____

_____

_____

_____

_____

7. **Below is a list of six characters you read about in "From the Elephant Pit." Read the list of words in the box. Choose the three words that best describe each character.**

Character Traits		
kind	grateful	friendly
honest	clever	truthful
caring	considerate	weak
ungrateful	angry	dishonest

**You may use the same words for more than one character.
You may also use your own words.
Write these words in the spaces provided.**

The Hunter

1._____

2._____

3._____

The Lion

1._____

2._____

3._____

The Man

1._____

2._____

3._____

The Falcon

1._____

2._____

3._____

The Mouse

1._____

2._____

3._____

The Snake

1._____

2._____

3._____

Directions   Today you will do a writing assignment. The poem below, "The Duel," may give you ideas for your writing. Read the poem to yourself while it is read to you.

The Duel

by Eugene Field

The gingham dog and the calico cat
Side by side on the table sat;
'Twas half-past twelve, and (what do you think!)
Nor one nor t' other had slept a wink!
The old Dutch clock and the Chinese plate
Appeared to know as sure as fate
There was going to be a terrible spat.

(I wasn't there; I simply state
What was told to me by the Chinese plate!)

The gingham dog went "bow-wow-wow!"
And the calico cat replied "mee-ow!"
The air was littered, an hour or so,
With bits of gingham and calico,
While the old Dutch clock in the chimney-place
Up with its hands before its face,
For it always dreaded a family row!

(Now mind: I'm only telling you
What the old Dutch clock declares is true!)

The Chinese plate looked very blue,
And wailed, "Oh, dear! What shall we do!"
But the gingham dog and the calico cat
Wallowed this way and tumbled that,
Employing every tooth and claw
In the awfullest way you ever saw
And oh! How the gingham and calico flew!

(Don't fancy I exaggerate—
I got my news from the Chinese plate!)

Next morning where the two had sat
They found no trace of dog or cat;
And some folks think unto this day
That burglars stole that pair away!
But the truth about the cat and pup
Is this: they ate each other up!

Now what do you really think—of that!

(The old Dutch clock it told me so,
And that is how I came to know.)

Writing to Explain—Personal Narrative

What kinds of toys do you have? Imagine that they were alive. What kind of adventures might they have? Write a story describing an adventure that one of your toys has. Be sure to use words that make your meaning clear. Your paper should include good elements and mechanics of writing.

- **What does your toy look like?**
- **How would this toy act if it was alive?**
- **When would the toy have a secret adventure?**
- **What kinds of things happen on this adventure?**
- **How can you write details to make your story a funny one?**

You may take notes, create a web, or do other prewriting work. Then write your narrative. Use your own paper or write in your literary response journal.

Here is a checklist for you to follow to help you do your best writing. Before you begin writing, read the checklist. Reread it as often as you need.

Writer's Checklist

Remember to

❏ Keep the central idea or topic in mind.

❏ Keep your audience in mind.

❏ Support your ideas with details, explanations, and examples.

❏ State your ideas in a clear sequence.

❏ Include an opening and a closing.

❏ Use a variety of words and vary your sentence structure.

❏ State your opinion or conclusion clearly.

❏ Capitalize, spell, and use punctuation correctly.

❏ Write neatly.

After you write your composition, read what you have written. Use the checklist to make certain that your writing is the best it can be.

Correlation to the New Jersey Core Curriculum Content Standards

This worktext is customized to the New Jersey Core Curriculum Content Standards and Cumulative Progress Indicators and will help you prepare for the New Jersey Grade Three Assessment of Skills and Knowledge (NJ ASK).

As the lesson for each Cumulative Progress Indicator (CPI) is completed, place a ✓ to indicate Mastery or an X to indicate Review Needed.

Unit 1: Reading and Viewing / Chapter 1: Guided Reading for a Narrative Selection	1	2	3	NA	NA	NA	NA	NA	NA	Un. Rev	End Rev
Standard 3.1 (Reading) All students will understand and apply the knowledge of sounds, letters, and words in written English to become independent and fluent readers, and will read a variety of materials and texts with fluency and comprehension.											
A1. CONCEPTS ABOUT PRINT/TEXT — Recognize that printed materials provide specific information.	★	★	✓							★	★
A2. CONCEPTS ABOUT PRINT/TEXT — Recognize purposes for print conventions such as end-sentence punctuation, paragraphing, and bold print.	★	✓	✓							★	★
A3. CONCEPTS ABOUT PRINT/TEXT — Use a glossary or index to locate information in a text.	○	★	✓							✓	✓
B1. PHONOLOGICAL AWARENESS (INCLUDES PHONEMIC AWARENESS) — Demonstrate a sophisticated sense of sound-symbol relationships, including all phonemes (e.g., blends, digraphs, dipthongs)	○	★	★							★	★
C1. DECODING AND WORD RECOGNITION — Know sounds for a range of prefixes and suffixes (e.g., re-, ex-, -ment, -tion).	○	★	★							★	★
C2. DECODING AND WORD RECOGNITION — Use letter-sound knowledge and structural analysis to decode words.	○	★	★							★	★
C3. DECODING AND WORD RECOGNITION — Use context to accurately read words with more than one pronunciation.	○	○	★							★	★
D1. FLUENCY — Recognize grade-level words accurately and with ease so that a text sounds like spoken language when read aloud.	○	★	✓							✓	✓
D2. FLUENCY — Read longer text and chapter books independently and silently.	○	★	★							★	★
D3. FLUENCY — Read aloud with proper phrasing, inflection, and intonation.	★	★	✓							✓	✓
E1. READING STRATEGIES (BEFORE, DURING, AFTER READING) — Set purpose for reading and check to verify or change predictions during/after reading.	★	★	★							★	★
E2. READING STRATEGIES (BEFORE, DURING, AFTER READING) — Monitor comprehension and accuracy while reading in context and self-correct errors.	○	★	★							★	★
E3. READING STRATEGIES (BEFORE, DURING, AFTER READING) — Use pictures and context clues to assist with decoding of new words.	○	★	★							★	★
E4. READING STRATEGIES (BEFORE, DURING, AFTER READING) — Develop and use graphic organizers to build on experiences and extend learning.	★	★	★							★	★
F1. VOCABULARY AND CONCEPT DEVELOPMENT — Spell previously studied words and spelling patterns accurately.	○	○	★							★	★
F3. VOCABULARY AND CONCEPT DEVELOPMENT — Infer word meanings from taught roots, prefixes, and suffixes.	○	○	★							★	★
F4. VOCABULARY AND CONCEPT DEVELOPMENT — Use a grade-appropriate dictionary with assistance from teacher.	○	○	★							✓	✓
G1. COMPREHENSION SKILLS AND RESPONSE TO TEXT — Recognize purpose of the text.	★	★	★							★	★
G2. COMPREHENSION SKILLS AND RESPONSE TO TEXT — Distinguish cause/effect, fact/opinion, main idea/supporting details in interpreting texts.	★	★	★							★	★

Column header notes: Review Skill / Mastered Skill / Lessons

★ Standards covered   ○ Standards to be covered   ✓ Standards previously covered

Correlation to the New Jersey Core Curriculum Content Standards

This worktext is customized to the New Jersey Core Curriculum Content Standards and Cumulative Progress Indicators and will help you prepare for the New Jersey Grade Three Assessment of Skills and Knowledge (NJ ASK).

As the lesson for each Cumulative Progress Indicator (CPI) is completed, place a ✓ to indicate Mastery or an X to indicate Review Needed.

Unit 1: Reading and Viewing — Chapter 1: Guided Reading for a Narrative Selection (cont.)	1	2	3	NA	NA	NA	NA	NA	NA	Un. Rev	End Rev
Standard 3.1 (Reading) All students will understand and apply the knowledge of sounds, letters, and words in written English to become independent and fluent readers, and will read a variety of materials and texts with fluency and comprehension.											
G3. Comprehension Skills and Response to Text — Interpret information in graphs, charts, and diagrams.	○	★	✓							★	★
G4. Comprehension Skills and Response to Text — Ask how, why, and what-if questions in interpreting nonfiction texts.	○	★	✓							★	★
G5. Comprehension Skills and Response to Text — Recognize how authors use humor, sarcasm, and imagery to extend meaning.	○	○	★							★	★
G6. Comprehension Skills and Response to Text — Discuss underlying theme or message in interpreting fiction.	★	✓	★							★	★
G7. Comprehension Skills and Response to Text — Summarize major points from fiction and nonfiction texts.	★	★	★							★	★
G8. Comprehension Skills and Response to Text — Draw conclusions and inferences from texts.	★	★	★							★	★
G9. Comprehension Skills and Response to Text — Recognize first-person "I" point of view.	★	✓	★							★	★
G10. Comprehension Skills and Response to Text — Compare and contrast story plots, characters, settings, and themes.	★	✓	★							★	★
G11. Comprehension Skills and Response to Text — Participate in creative responses to texts (e.g., dramatizations, oral presentations).	★	✓	✓							✓	✓
G12. Comprehension Skills and Response to Text — Read regularly in materials appropriate for their independent reading level.	★	★	✓							✓	✓
G14. Comprehension Skills and Response to Text — Use information and reasoning to examine bases of hypotheses and opinions.	○	★	✓							★	✓
H2. Inquiry and Research — Draw conclusions from information and data gathered.	★	★	✓							★	✓
H3. Inquiry and Research — Read a variety of nonfiction and fiction books and produce evidence of understanding.	○	○	★							★	✓
Standard 3.2 (Writing) All students will write in clear, concise, organized language that varies in content and form for different audiences and purposes.											
A1. Writing as a Process (prewriting, drafting, revising, editing, postwriting) — Generate possible ideas for writing through recalling experiences, listening to stories, reading, brainstorming, and discussion.	○	★	★							★	★
A2. Writing as a Process (prewriting, drafting, revising, editing, postwriting) — Examine real-world examples of writing in various genres to gain understanding of how authors communicate ideas through form, structure, and author's voice.	★	✓	✓							✓	✓
A3. Writing as a Process (prewriting, drafting, revising, editing, postwriting) — Use graphic organizers to assist with planning writing.	○	○	★							★	★
C3. Mechanics, Spelling, Handwriting — Study examples of narrative and expository writing to develop understanding of paragraphs and indentation.	★	✓	✓							✓	✓
D7. Writing Forms, Audiences, and Purposes (exploring a variety of forms) — Respond to literature through writing to demonstrate an understanding of a text.	★	✓	★							★	★

★ Standards covered   ○ Standards to be covered   ✓ Standards previously covered

Correlation to the New Jersey Core Curriculum Content Standards

This worktext is customized to the New Jersey Core Curriculum Content Standards and Cumulative Progress Indicators and will help you prepare for the New Jersey Grade Three Assessment of Skills and Knowledge (NJ ASK).

As the lesson for each Cumulative Progress Indicator (CPI) is completed, place a ✓ to indicate Mastery or an X to indicate Review Needed.

Unit 1: Reading and Viewing Chapter 1: Guided Reading for a Narrative Selection (cont.)	Review Skill / Mastered Skill / Lessons: 1	2	3	NA	NA	NA	NA	NA	NA	Un. Rev	End Rev
Standard 3.3 (Speaking) All students will speak in clear, concise, organized language that varies in content and form for different audiences and purposes.											
A1. Discussion (small group and whole class) Listen and follow a discussion in order to contribute appropriately.	○	★	✓							✓	✓
A4. Discussion (small group and whole class) Support an opinion with details.	○	★	✓							✓	✓
C1. Word Choice Use vocabulary related to a particular topic.	★	★	✓							✓	✓
C2. Word Choice Adapt language to persuade, explain, or seek information.	★	✓	✓							✓	✓
C3. Word Choice Use new vocabulary and figurative language learned from literature and classroom experiences.	○	★	✓							✓	✓
Standard 3.4 (Listening) All students will listen actively to information from a variety of sources in a variety of situations.											
B2. Listening Comprehension Listen to a story read aloud and/or information from television or film, and summarize main ideas.	★	✓	✓							✓	✓
B3. Listening Comprehension Paraphrase information shared by others.	★	✓	✓							✓	✓
Standard 3.5 (Viewing and Media Literacy) All students will access, view, evaluate, and respond to print, nonprint, and electronic texts and resources.											
A1. Constructing Meaning Begin to demonstrate an awareness of different media forms and how they contribute to communication.	★	✓	✓							✓	✓
A2. Constructing Meaning Identify the central theme and main ideas in different media.	★	★	✓							✓	✓
B1. Visual and Verbal Messages Recognize the effects of visual arts on one's mood and emotions.	★	★	✓							✓	✓
B2. Visual and Verbal Messages Begin to explore and interpret messages found in advertisements and other texts.	★	✓	✓							✓	✓

Unit 1: Reading and Viewing Chapter 2: Guided Reading for Everyday and Persuasive Selections	Review Skill / Mastered Skill / Lessons: 1	2	3	NA	NA	NA	NA	NA	NA	Un. Rev	End Rev
Standard 3.1 (Reading) All students will understand and apply the knowledge of sounds, letters, and words in written English to become independent and fluent readers, and will read a variety of materials and texts with fluency and comprehension.											
A1. Concepts About Print/Text Recognize that printed materials provide specific information.	★	★	✓							★	★
A3. Concepts About Print/Text Use a glossary or index to locate information in a text.	✓	★	✓							✓	✓
B1. Phonological Awareness (includes phonemic awareness) Demonstrate a sophisticated sense of sound-symbol relationships, including all phonemes (e.g., blends, digraphs, dipthongs)	✓	★	★							★	★

★ Standards covered ○ Standards to be covered ✓ Standards previously covered

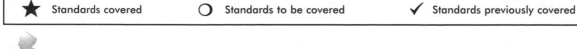

Correlation to the New Jersey Core Curriculum Content Standards

This worktext is customized to the New Jersey Core Curriculum Content Standards and Cumulative Progress Indicators and will help you prepare for the New Jersey Grade Three Assessment of Skills and Knowledge (NJ ASK).

As the lesson for each Cumulative Progress Indicator (CPI) is completed, place a ✔ to indicate Mastery or an X to indicate Review Needed.

Unit 1: Reading and Viewing — Review Skill / Mastered Skill / Lessons Chapter 2: Guided Reading for Everyday and Persuasive Selections (cont.)	1	2	3	NA	NA	NA	NA	NA	NA	Un. Rev	End Rev
Standard 3.1 (Reading) All students will understand and apply the knowledge of sounds, letters, and words in written English to become independent and fluent readers, and will read a variety of materials and texts with fluency and comprehension.											
C1. Decoding and Word Recognition Know sounds for a range of prefixes and suffixes (e.g., re-, ex-, -ment, -tion).	✔	★	★							★	★
C2. Decoding and Word Recognition Use letter-sound knowledge and structural analysis to decode words.	✔	★	★							★	★
C3. Decoding and Word Recognition Use context to accurately read words with more than one pronunciation.	✔	★	★							★	★
D1. Fluency Recognize grade-level words accurately and with ease so that a text sounds like spoken language when read aloud.	★	★	✔							✔	✔
D2. Fluency Read longer text and chapter books independently and silently.	✔	★	★							★	★
D3. Fluency Read aloud with proper phrasing, inflection, and intonation.	★	★	✔							✔	✔
E1. Reading Strategies (before, during, after reading) Set purpose for reading and check to verify or change predictions during/after reading.	★	★	★							★	★
E2. Reading Strategies (before, during, after reading) Monitor comprehension and accuracy while reading in context and self-correct errors.	✔	★	★							★	★
E3. Reading Strategies (before, during, after reading) Use pictures and context clues to assist with decoding of new words.	✔	★	★							★	★
E4. Reading Strategies (before, during, after reading) Develop and use graphic organizers to build on experiences and extend learning.	★	★	★							★	★
F1. Vocabulary and Concept Development Spell previously studied words and spelling patterns accurately.	✔	★	★							★	★
F2. Vocabulary and Concept Development Point to or clearly identify specific words or wording that are causing comprehension difficulties.	○	★	✔							★	★
F3. Vocabulary and Concept Development Infer word meanings from taught roots, prefixes, and suffixes.	✔	★	★							★	★
F4. Vocabulary and Concept Development Use a grade-appropriate dictionary with assistance from teacher.	✔	★	★							✔	✔
F5. Vocabulary and Concept Development Use pictures and context clues to assist with meaning of new words.	○	★	★							★	★
G1. Comprehension Skills and Response to Text Recognize purpose of the text.	★	★	★							★	★
G2. Comprehension Skills and Response to Text Distinguish cause/effect, fact/opinion, main idea/supporting details in interpreting texts.	★	★	★							★	★
G3. Comprehension Skills and Response to Text Interpret information in graphs, charts, and diagrams.	★	★	★							★	★

★ Standards covered   ○ Standards to be covered   ✔ Standards previously covered

Correlation to the New Jersey Core Curriculum Content Standards

This worktext is customized to the New Jersey Core Curriculum Content Standards and Cumulative Progress Indicators and will help you prepare for the New Jersey Grade Three Assessment of Skills and Knowledge (NJ ASK).

As the lesson for each Cumulative Progress Indicator (CPI) is completed, place a ✓ to indicate Mastery or an X to indicate Review Needed.

Unit 1: Reading and Viewing Chapter 2: Guided Reading for Everyday and Persuasive Selections (cont.)	1	2	3	NA	NA	NA	NA	NA	NA	Un. Rev	End Rev
Standard 3.1 (Reading) All students will understand and apply the knowledge of sounds, letters, and words in written English to become independent and fluent readers, and will read a variety of materials and texts with fluency and comprehension.											
G4. COMPREHENSION SKILLS AND RESPONSE TO TEXT — Ask how, why, and what-if questions in interpreting nonfiction texts.	★	★	★							★	★
G6. COMPREHENSION SKILLS AND RESPONSE TO TEXT — Discuss underlying theme or message in interpreting fiction.	✓	✓	★							★	★
G7. COMPREHENSION SKILLS AND RESPONSE TO TEXT — Summarize major points from fiction and nonfiction texts.	★	★	★							★	★
G8. COMPREHENSION SKILLS AND RESPONSE TO TEXT — Draw conclusions and inferences from texts.	★	★	★							★	★
G10. COMPREHENSION SKILLS AND RESPONSE TO TEXT — Compare and contrast story plots, characters, settings, and themes.	✓	✓	★							★	★
G12. COMPREHENSION SKILLS AND RESPONSE TO TEXT — Read regularly in materials appropriate for their independent reading level.	★	★	✓							✓	✓
G13. COMPREHENSION SKILLS AND RESPONSE TO TEXT — Read and comprehend both fiction and nonfiction books and produce evidence of understanding.	○	★	★							★	✓
G14. COMPREHENSION SKILLS AND RESPONSE TO TEXT — Use information and reasoning to examine bases of hypotheses and opinions.	★	★	★							★	✓
H2. INQUIRY AND RESEARCH — Draw conclusions from information and data gathered.	★	✓	✓							★	✓
H3. INQUIRY AND RESEARCH — Read a variety of nonfiction and fiction books and produce evidence of understanding.	✓	★	★							★	✓
Standard 3.2 (Writing) All students will write in clear, concise, organized language that varies in content and form for different audiences and purposes.											
A1. WRITING AS A PROCESS (PREWRITING, DRAFTING, REVISING, EDITING, POSTWRITING) — Generate possible ideas for writing through recalling experiences, listening to stories, reading, brainstorming, and discussion.	✓	✓	★							★	★
A2. WRITING AS A PROCESS (PREWRITING, DRAFTING, REVISING, EDITING, POSTWRITING) — Examine real-world examples of writing in various genres to gain understanding of how authors communicate ideas through form, structure, and author's voice.	★	✓	✓							✓	✓
A3. WRITING AS A PROCESS (PREWRITING, DRAFTING, REVISING, EDITING, POSTWRITING) — Use graphic organizers to assist with planning writing.	✓	✓	★							★	★
C3. MECHANICS, SPELLING, HANDWRITING — Study examples of narrative and expository writing to develop understanding of paragraphs and indentation.	★	✓	✓							✓	✓
D7. WRITING FORMS, AUDIENCES, AND PURPOSES (EXPLORING A VARIETY OF FORMS) — Respond to literature through writing to demonstrate an understanding of a text.	★	✓	★							★	★
Standard 3.3 (Speaking) All students will speak in clear, concise, organized language that varies in content and form for different audiences and purposes.											
A1. DISCUSSION (SMALL GROUP AND WHOLE CLASS) — Listen and follow a discussion in order to contribute appropriately.	✓	★	✓							✓	✓
A4. DISCUSSION (SMALL GROUP AND WHOLE CLASS) — Support an opinion with details.	✓	★	✓							✓	✓

★ Standards covered   ○ Standards to be covered   ✓ Standards previously covered

Correlation to the New Jersey Core Curriculum Content Standards

This worktext is customized to the New Jersey Core Curriculum Content Standards and Cumulative Progress Indicators and will help you prepare for the New Jersey Grade Three Assessment of Skills and Knowledge (NJ ASK).

As the lesson for each Cumulative Progress Indicator (CPI) is completed, place a ✓ to indicate Mastery or an X to indicate Review Needed.

Unit 1: Reading and Viewing
Chapter 2: Guided Reading for Everyday and Persuasive Selections (cont.)

Review Skill / Mastered Skill / Lessons

	1	2	3	NA	NA	NA	NA	NA	NA	Un. Rev	End Rev
Standard 3.3 (Speaking) All students will speak in clear, concise, organized language that varies in content and form for different audiences and purposes.											
C1. WORD CHOICE Use vocabulary related to a particular topic.	★	★	✓							✓	✓
C2. WORD CHOICE Adapt language to persuade, explain, or seek information.	★	✓	✓							✓	✓
C3. WORD CHOICE Use new vocabulary and figurative language learned from literature and classroom experiences.	✓	★	✓							✓	✓
Standard 3.4 (Listening) All students will listen actively to information from a variety of sources in a variety of situations.											
B2. LISTENING COMPREHENSION Listen to a story read aloud and/or information from television or film, and summarize main ideas.	★	✓	✓							✓	✓
B3. LISTENING COMPREHENSION Paraphrase information shared by others.	★	✓	✓							✓	✓
Standard 3.5 (Viewing and Media Literacy) All students will access, view, evaluate, and respond to print, nonprint, and electronic texts and resources.											
A1. CONSTRUCTING MEANING Begin to demonstrate an awareness of different media forms and how they contribute to communication.	★	✓	✓							✓	✓
A2. CONSTRUCTING MEANING Identify the central theme and main ideas in different media.	★	★	✓							✓	✓
B1. VISUAL AND VERBAL MESSAGES Recognize the effects of visual arts on one's mood and emotions.	★	★	✓							✓	✓
B2. VISUAL AND VERBAL MESSAGES Begin to explore and interpret messages found in advertisements and other texts.	★	✓	✓							✓	✓

Unit 1: Reading and Viewing
Chapter 3: Guided Reading for an Informational Selection

Review Skill / Mastered Skill / Lessons

	1	2	3	NA	NA	NA	NA	NA	NA	Un. Rev	End Rev
Standard 3.1 (Reading) All students will understand and apply the knowledge of sounds, letters, and words in written English to become independent and fluent readers, and will read a variety of materials and texts with fluency and comprehension.											
A1. CONCEPTS ABOUT PRINT/TEXT Recognize that printed materials provide specific information.	★	★	✓							★	★
A2. CONCEPTS ABOUT PRINT/TEXT Recognize purposes for print conventions such as end-sentence punctuation, paragraphing, and bold print.	★	✓	✓							★	★
A3. CONCEPTS ABOUT PRINT/TEXT Use a glossary or index to locate information in a text.	✓	★	✓							✓	✓
B1. PHONOLOGICAL AWARENESS (INCLUDES PHONEMIC AWARENESS) Demonstrate a sophisticated sense of sound-symbol relationships, including all phonemes (e.g., blends, digraphs, dipthongs)	✓	★	★							★	★
C1. DECODING AND WORD RECOGNITION Know sounds for a range of prefixes and suffixes (e.g., re-, ex-, -ment, -tion).	✓	★	★							★	★

★ Standards covered   ○ Standards to be covered   ✓ Standards previously covered

Correlation to the New Jersey Core Curriculum Content Standards

This worktext is customized to the New Jersey Core Curriculum Content Standards and Cumulative Progress Indicators and will help you prepare for the New Jersey Grade Three Assessment of Skills and Knowledge (NJ ASK).

As the lesson for each Cumulative Progress Indicator (CPI) is completed, place a ✔ to indicate Mastery or an X to indicate Review Needed.

Unit 1: Reading and Viewing — Chapter 3: Guided Reading for an Informational Selection (cont.)	1	2	3	NA	NA	NA	NA	NA	NA	Un. Rev	End Rev
Standard 3.1 (Reading) All students will understand and apply the knowledge of sounds, letters, and words in written English to become independent and fluent readers, and will read a variety of materials and texts with fluency and comprehension.											
C2. DECODING AND WORD RECOGNITION Use letter-sound knowledge and structural analysis to decode words.	✔	★	★							★	★
C3. DECODING AND WORD RECOGNITION Use context to accurately read words with more than one pronunciation.	✔	★	★							★	★
D1. FLUENCY Recognize grade-level words accurately and with ease so that a text sounds like spoken language when read aloud.	★	★	✔							✔	✔
D2. FLUENCY Read longer text and chapter books independently and silently.	✔	★	★							★	★
D3. FLUENCY Read aloud with proper phrasing, inflection, and intonation.	★	★	✔							✔	✔
E1. READING STRATEGIES (BEFORE, DURING, AFTER READING) Set purpose for reading and check to verify or change predictions during/after reading.	★	★	★							★	★
E2. READING STRATEGIES (BEFORE, DURING, AFTER READING) Monitor comprehension and accuracy while reading in context and self-correct errors.	✔	★	★							★	★
E3. READING STRATEGIES (BEFORE, DURING, AFTER READING) Use pictures and context clues to assist with decoding of new words.	✔	★	★							★	★
E4. READING STRATEGIES (BEFORE, DURING, AFTER READING) Develop and use graphic organizers to build on experiences and extend learning.	★	★	★							★	★
F1. VOCABULARY AND CONCEPT DEVELOPMENT Spell previously studied words and spelling patterns accurately.	✔	★	★							★	★
F2. VOCABULARY AND CONCEPT DEVELOPMENT Point to or clearly identify specific words or wording that are causing comprehension difficulties.	✔	★	✔							★	★
F3. VOCABULARY AND CONCEPT DEVELOPMENT Infer word meanings from taught roots, prefixes, and suffixes.	✔	★	★							★	★
F4. VOCABULARY AND CONCEPT DEVELOPMENT Use a grade-appropriate dictionary with assistance from teacher.	✔	★	★							✔	✔
F5. VOCABULARY AND CONCEPT DEVELOPMENT Use pictures and context clues to assist with meaning of new words.	✔	★	✔							★	★
G1. COMPREHENSION SKILLS AND RESPONSE TO TEXT Recognize purpose of the text.	★	★	★							★	★
G2. COMPREHENSION SKILLS AND RESPONSE TO TEXT Distinguish cause/effect, fact/opinion, main idea/supporting details in interpreting texts.	★	★	★							★	★
G3. COMPREHENSION SKILLS AND RESPONSE TO TEXT Interpret information in graphs, charts, and diagrams.	✔	★	★							★	★
G4. COMPREHENSION SKILLS AND RESPONSE TO TEXT Ask how, why, and what-if questions in interpreting nonfiction texts.	★	★	★							★	★
G6. COMPREHENSION SKILLS AND RESPONSE TO TEXT Discuss underlying theme or message in interpreting fiction.	✔	✔	★							★	★

★ Standards covered   O Standards to be covered   ✔ Standards previously covered

Correlation to the New Jersey Core Curriculum Content Standards

This worktext is customized to the New Jersey Core Curriculum Content Standards and Cumulative Progress Indicators and will help you prepare for the New Jersey Grade Three Assessment of Skills and Knowledge (NJ ASK).

As the lesson for each Cumulative Progress Indicator (CPI) is completed, place a ✓ to indicate Mastery or an X to indicate Review Needed.

Unit 1: Reading and Viewing — Chapter 3: Guided Reading for an Informational Selection (cont.)	1	2	3	NA	NA	NA	NA	NA	NA	Un. Rev	End Rev
Standard 3.1 (Reading) All students will understand and apply the knowledge of sounds, letters, and words in written English to become independent and fluent readers, and will read a variety of materials and texts with fluency and comprehension.											
G7. COMPREHENSION SKILLS AND RESPONSE TO TEXT Summarize major points from fiction and nonfiction texts.	★	★	★							★	★
G8. COMPREHENSION SKILLS AND RESPONSE TO TEXT Draw conclusions and inferences from texts.	★	★	★							★	★
G10. COMPREHENSION SKILLS AND RESPONSE TO TEXT Compare and contrast story plots, characters, settings, and themes.	✓	✓	★							★	★
G12. COMPREHENSION SKILLS AND RESPONSE TO TEXT Read regularly in materials appropriate for their independent reading level.	★	★	✓							✓	✓
G13. COMPREHENSION SKILLS AND RESPONSE TO TEXT Read and comprehend both fiction and nonfiction books and produce evidence of understanding.	✓	★	★							★	✓
G14. COMPREHENSION SKILLS AND RESPONSE TO TEXT Use information and reasoning to examine bases of hypotheses and opinions.	✓	★	★							★	✓
H2. INQUIRY AND RESEARCH Draw conclusions from information and data gathered.	★	✓	✓							★	✓
H3. INQUIRY AND RESEARCH Read a variety of nonfiction and fiction books and produce evidence of understanding.	✓	★	★							★	✓
Standard 3.2 (Writing) All students will write in clear, concise, organized language that varies in content and form for different audiences and purposes.											
A1. WRITING AS A PROCESS (PREWRITING, DRAFTING, REVISING, EDITING, POSTWRITING) Generate possible ideas for writing through recalling experiences, listening to stories, reading, brainstorming, and discussion.	✓	✓	★							★	★
A2. WRITING AS A PROCESS (PREWRITING, DRAFTING, REVISING, EDITING, POSTWRITING) Examine real-world examples of writing in various genres to gain understanding of how authors communicate ideas through form, structure, and author's voice.	★	✓	✓							✓	✓
A3. WRITING AS A PROCESS (PREWRITING, DRAFTING, REVISING, EDITING, POSTWRITING) Use graphic organizers to assist with planning writing.	✓	✓	★							★	★
C3. MECHANICS, SPELLING, HANDWRITING Study examples of narrative and expository writing to develop understanding of paragraphs and indentation.	★	✓	✓							✓	✓
D7. WRITING FORMS, AUDIENCES, AND PURPOSES (EXPLORING A VARIETY OF FORMS) Respond to literature through writing to demonstrate an understanding of a text.	★	✓	★							★	★
Standard 3.3 (Speaking) All students will speak in clear, concise, organized language that varies in content and form for different audiences and purposes.											
A1. DISCUSSION (SMALL GROUP AND WHOLE CLASS) Listen and follow a discussion in order to contribute appropriately.	✓	★	✓							✓	✓
A4. DISCUSSION (SMALL GROUP AND WHOLE CLASS) Support an opinion with details.	★	★	✓							✓	✓
C1. WORD CHOICE Use vocabulary related to a particular topic.	★	★	✓							✓	✓
C2. WORD CHOICE Adapt language to persuade, explain, or seek information.	★	✓	✓							✓	✓

★ Standards covered   O Standards to be covered   ✓ Standards previously covered

Correlation to the New Jersey Core Curriculum Content Standards

This worktext is customized to the New Jersey Core Curriculum Content Standards and Cumulative Progress Indicators and will help you prepare for the New Jersey Grade Three Assessment of Skills and Knowledge (NJ ASK).

As the lesson for each Cumulative Progress Indicator (CPI) is completed, place a ✓ to indicate Mastery or an X to indicate Review Needed.

Unit 1: Reading and Viewing Chapter 3: Guided Reading for an Informational Selection (cont.)	Review Skill Mastered Skill Lessons	1	2	3	NA	NA	NA	NA	NA	NA	Un. Rev	End Rev
Standard 3.3 (Speaking) All students will speak in clear, concise, organized language that varies in content and form for different audiences and purposes.												
C3. WORD CHOICE Use new vocabulary and figurative language learned from literature and classroom experiences.		✓	★	✓							✓	✓
Standard 3.4 (Listening) All students will listen actively to information from a variety of sources in a variety of situations.												
B2. LISTENING COMPREHENSION Listen to a story read aloud and/or information from television or film, and summarize main ideas.		★	✓	✓							✓	✓
B3. LISTENING COMPREHENSION Paraphrase information shared by others.		★	✓	✓							✓	✓
Standard 3.5 (Viewing and Media Literacy) All students will access, view, evaluate, and respond to print, nonprint, and electronic texts and resources.												
A1. CONSTRUCTING MEANING Begin to demonstrate an awareness of different media forms and how they contribute to communication.		★	✓	✓							✓	✓
A2. CONSTRUCTING MEANING Identify the central theme and main ideas in different media.		★	★	✓							✓	✓
B1. VISUAL AND VERBAL MESSAGES Recognize the effects of visual arts on one's mood and emotions.		★	★	✓							✓	✓
B2. VISUAL AND VERBAL MESSAGES Begin to explore and interpret messages found in advertisements and other texts.		★	✓	✓							✓	✓
Unit 1: Reading and Viewing Chapter 4: Guided Reading for a Poem	Review Skill Mastered Skill Lessons	1	2	3	NA	NA	NA	NA	NA	NA	Un. Rev	End Rev
Standard 3.1 (Reading) All students will understand and apply the knowledge of sounds, letters, and words in written English to become independent and fluent readers, and will read a variety of materials and texts with fluency and comprehension.												
A1. CONCEPTS ABOUT PRINT/TEXT Recognize that printed materials provide specific information.		★	★	✓							★	★
A2. CONCEPTS ABOUT PRINT/TEXT Recognize purposes for print conventions such as end-sentence punctuation, paragraphing, and bold print.		★	✓	✓							★	★
A3. CONCEPTS ABOUT PRINT/TEXT Use a glossary or index to locate information in a text.		✓	★	✓							✓	✓
B1. PHONOLOGICAL AWARENESS (INCLUDES PHONEMIC AWARENESS) Demonstrate a sophisticated sense of sound-symbol relationships, including all phonemes (e.g., blends, digraphs, dipthongs)		✓	★	★							★	★
C1. DECODING AND WORD RECOGNITION Know sounds for a range of prefixes and suffixes (e.g., re-, ex-, -ment, -tion).		✓	★	★							★	★
C2. DECODING AND WORD RECOGNITION Use letter-sound knowledge and structural analysis to decode words.		✓	★	★							★	★
C3. DECODING AND WORD RECOGNITION Use context to accurately read words with more than one pronunciation.		✓	★	★							★	★

★ Standards covered	○ Standards to be covered	✓ Standards previously covered

Correlation to the New Jersey Core Curriculum Content Standards

This worktext is customized to the New Jersey Core Curriculum Content Standards and Cumulative Progress Indicators and will help you prepare for the New Jersey Grade Three Assessment of Skills and Knowledge (NJ ASK).

As the lesson for each Cumulative Progress Indicator (CPI) is completed, place a ✓ to indicate Mastery or an X to indicate Review Needed.

Unit 1: Reading and Viewing Chapter 4: Guided Reading for a Poem (cont.)	Review Skill Mastered Skill Lessons	1	2	3	NA	NA	NA	NA	NA	NA	Un. Rev	End Rev
Standard 3.1 (Reading) All students will understand and apply the knowledge of sounds, letters, and words in written English to become independent and fluent readers, and will read a variety of materials and texts with fluency and comprehension.												
D1. FLUENCY Recognize grade-level words accurately and with ease so that a text sounds like spoken language when read aloud.		★	★	✓							✓	✓
D2. FLUENCY Read longer text and chapter books independently and silently.		✓	★	★							★	★
D3. FLUENCY Read aloud with proper phrasing, inflection, and intonation.		★	★	✓							✓	✓
E1. READING STRATEGIES (BEFORE, DURING, AFTER READING) Set purpose for reading and check to verify or change predictions during/after reading.		★	★	★							★	★
E2. READING STRATEGIES (BEFORE, DURING, AFTER READING) Monitor comprehension and accuracy while reading in context and self-correct errors.		✓	★	★							★	★
E3. READING STRATEGIES (BEFORE, DURING, AFTER READING) Use pictures and context clues to assist with decoding of new words.		✓	★	★							★	★
E4. READING STRATEGIES (BEFORE, DURING, AFTER READING) Develop and use graphic organizers to build on experiences and extend learning.		★	★	★							★	★
F1. VOCABULARY AND CONCEPT DEVELOPMENT Spell previously studied words and spelling patterns accurately.		✓	★	★							★	★
F2. VOCABULARY AND CONCEPT DEVELOPMENT Point to or clearly identify specific words or wording that are causing comprehension difficulties.		✓	★	✓							★	★
F3. VOCABULARY AND CONCEPT DEVELOPMENT Infer word meanings from taught roots, prefixes, and suffixes.		✓	★	★							★	★
F4. VOCABULARY AND CONCEPT DEVELOPMENT Use a grade-appropriate dictionary with assistance from teacher.		✓	★	★							✓	✓
F5. VOCABULARY AND CONCEPT DEVELOPMENT Use pictures and context clues to assist with meaning of new words.		✓	★	★							★	★
G1. COMPREHENSION SKILLS AND RESPONSE TO TEXT Recognize purpose of the text.		★	★	★							★	★
G2. COMPREHENSION SKILLS AND RESPONSE TO TEXT Distinguish cause/effect, fact/opinion, main idea/supporting details in interpreting texts.		★	★	★							★	★
G5. COMPREHENSION SKILLS AND RESPONSE TO TEXT Recognize how authors use humor, sarcasm, and imagery to extend meaning.		✓	★	★							★	★
G6. COMPREHENSION SKILLS AND RESPONSE TO TEXT Discuss underlying theme or message in interpreting fiction.		★	★	★							★	★
G7. COMPREHENSION SKILLS AND RESPONSE TO TEXT Summarize major points from fiction and nonfiction texts.		★	★	★							★	★
G8. COMPREHENSION SKILLS AND RESPONSE TO TEXT Draw conclusions and inferences from texts.		★	★	★							★	★
G9. COMPREHENSION SKILLS AND RESPONSE TO TEXT Recognize first-person "I" point of view.		★	★	★							★	★

★ Standards covered   ◯ Standards to be covered   ✓ Standards previously covered

Correlation to the New Jersey Core Curriculum Content Standards

This worktext is customized to the New Jersey Core Curriculum Content Standards and Cumulative Progress Indicators and will help you prepare for the New Jersey Grade Three Assessment of Skills and Knowledge (NJ ASK).

As the lesson for each Cumulative Progress Indicator (CPI) is completed, place a ✓ to indicate Mastery or an X to indicate Review Needed.

Unit 1: Reading and Viewing — Chapter 4: Guided Reading for a Poem (cont.)	1	2	3	NA	NA	NA	NA	NA	NA	Un. Rev	End Rev
Standard 3.1 (Reading) All students will understand and apply the knowledge of sounds, letters, and words in written English to become independent and fluent readers, and will read a variety of materials and texts with fluency and comprehension.											
G10. COMPREHENSION SKILLS AND RESPONSE TO TEXT — Compare and contrast story plots, characters, settings, and themes.	★	★	★							★	★
G11. COMPREHENSION SKILLS AND RESPONSE TO TEXT — Participate in creative responses to texts (e.g., dramatizations, oral presentations).	★	★	✓							✓	✓
G12. COMPREHENSION SKILLS AND RESPONSE TO TEXT — Read regularly in materials appropriate for their independent reading level.	★	★	✓							✓	✓
G13. COMPREHENSION SKILLS AND RESPONSE TO TEXT — Read and comprehend both fiction and nonfiction books and produce evidence of understanding.	★	★	★							★	✓
H2. INQUIRY AND RESEARCH — Draw conclusions from information and data gathered.	★	✓	✓							★	✓
H3. INQUIRY AND RESEARCH — Read a variety of nonfiction and fiction books and produce evidence of understanding.	✓	★	★							★	✓
Standard 3.2 (Writing) All students will write in clear, concise, organized language that varies in content and form for different audiences and purposes.											
A1. WRITING AS A PROCESS (PREWRITING, DRAFTING, REVISING, EDITING, POSTWRITING) — Generate possible ideas for writing through recalling experiences, listening to stories, reading, brainstorming, and discussion.	✓	✓	★							★	★
A2. WRITING AS A PROCESS (PREWRITING, DRAFTING, REVISING, EDITING, POSTWRITING) — Examine real-world examples of writing in various genres to gain understanding of how authors communicate ideas through form, structure, and author's voice.	★	✓	✓							✓	✓
A3. WRITING AS A PROCESS (PREWRITING, DRAFTING, REVISING, EDITING, POSTWRITING) — Use graphic organizers to assist with planning writing.	✓	✓	★							★	★
C3. MECHANICS, SPELLING, HANDWRITING — Study examples of narrative and expository writing to develop understanding of paragraphs and indentation.	★	✓	✓							✓	✓
D7. WRITING FORMS, AUDIENCES, AND PURPOSES (EXPLORING A VARIETY OF FORMS) — Respond to literature through writing to demonstrate an understanding of a text.	★	✓	★							★	★
Standard 3.3 (Speaking) All students will speak in clear, concise, organized language that varies in content and form for different audiences and purposes.											
A1. DISCUSSION (SMALL GROUP AND WHOLE CLASS) — Listen and follow a discussion in order to contribute appropriately.	✓	★	✓							✓	✓
A4. DISCUSSION (SMALL GROUP AND WHOLE CLASS) — Support an opinion with details.	✓	★	✓							✓	✓
B2. LISTENING COMPREHENSION — Listen to a story read aloud and/or information from television or film, and summarize main ideas.	★	★	✓							✓	✓
B3. LISTENING COMPREHENSION — Paraphrase information shared by others.	★	✓	✓							✓	✓
Standard 3.4 (Listening) All students will listen actively to information from a variety of sources in a variety of situations.											
A1. ACTIVE LISTENING — Connect messages heard to prior knowledge and experiences.	★	★	✓							✓	✓

★ Standards covered   O Standards to be covered   ✓ Standards previously covered

Correlation to the New Jersey Core Curriculum Content Standards

This worktext is customized to the New Jersey Core Curriculum Content Standards and Cumulative Progress Indicators and will help you prepare for the New Jersey Grade Three Assessment of Skills and Knowledge (NJ ASK).

As the lesson for each Cumulative Progress Indicator (CPI) is completed, place a ✓ to indicate Mastery or an X to indicate Review Needed.

Unit 1: Reading and Viewing — Chapter 4: Guided Reading for a Poem (cont.)	1	2	3	NA	NA	NA	NA	NA	NA	Un. Rev	End Rev
Standard 3.4 (Listening) All students will listen actively to information from a variety of sources in a variety of situations.											
A2. ACTIVE LISTENING Exchange information through verbal and nonverbal messages.	✓	★	✓							✓	✓
B2. LISTENING COMPREHENSION Listen to a story read aloud and/or information from television or film, and summarize main ideas.	★	✓	✓							✓	✓
B3. LISTENING COMPREHENSION Paraphrase information shared by others.	★	★	✓							✓	✓
Standard 3.5 (Viewing and Media Literacy) All students will access, view, evaluate, and respond to print, nonprint, and electronic texts and resources.											
A1. CONSTRUCTING MEANING Begin to demonstrate an awareness of different media forms and how they contribute to communication.	★	✓	✓							✓	✓
A2. CONSTRUCTING MEANING Identify the central theme and main ideas in different media.	★	★	✓							✓	✓
B1. VISUAL AND VERBAL MESSAGES Recognize the effects of visual arts on one's mood and emotions.	★	★	✓							✓	✓
B2. VISUAL AND VERBAL MESSAGES Begin to explore and interpret messages found in advertisements and other texts.	★	✓	✓							✓	✓

Unit 2: Writing — Chapter 1: Prewriting	1	2	3	4	5	6	7	8	9	Un. Rev	End Rev
Standard 3.1 (Reading) All students will understand and apply the knowledge of sounds, letters, and words in written English to become independent and fluent readers, and will read a variety of materials and texts with fluency and comprehension.											
H1. INQUIRY AND RESEARCH Use library classification systems, print or electronic, to locate information.	○	○	○	○	○	★	✓	✓	✓	✓	✓
H2. INQUIRY AND RESEARCH Draw conclusions from information and data gathered.	✓	✓	✓	✓	✓	✓	✓	★	✓	✓	✓
H3. INQUIRY AND RESEARCH Read a variety of nonfiction and fiction books and produce evidence of understanding.	✓	✓	✓	✓	✓	✓	★	✓	✓	✓	✓
Standard 3.2 (Writing) All students will write in clear, concise, organized language that varies in content and form for different audiences and purposes.											
A1. WRITING AS A PROCESS (PREWRITING, DRAFTING, REVISING, EDITING, POSTWRITING) Generate possible ideas for writing through recalling experiences, listening to stories, reading, brainstorming, and discussion.	✓	✓	✓	✓	★	✓	✓	✓	✓	★	★
A2. WRITING AS A PROCESS (PREWRITING, DRAFTING, REVISING, EDITING, POSTWRITING) Examine real-world examples of writing in various genres to gain understanding of how authors communicate ideas through form, structure, and author's voice.	★	★	★	✓	✓	✓	✓	✓	✓	✓	✓
A3. WRITING AS A PROCESS (PREWRITING, DRAFTING, REVISING, EDITING, POSTWRITING) Use graphic organizers to assist with planning writing.	✓	✓	✓	✓	★	✓	★	★	★	★	★
A8. WRITING AS A PROCESS (PREWRITING, DRAFTING, REVISING, EDITING, POSTWRITING) Begin to develop author's voice in own writing.	○	○	○	★	✓	✓	✓	✓	✓	★	★

★ Standards covered   ○ Standards to be covered   ✓ Standards previously covered

Correlation to the New Jersey Core Curriculum Content Standards

This worktext is customized to the New Jersey Core Curriculum Content Standards and Cumulative Progress Indicators and will help you prepare for the New Jersey Grade Three Assessment of Skills and Knowledge (NJ ASK).

As the lesson for each Cumulative Progress Indicator (CPI) is completed, place a ✓ to indicate Mastery or an X to indicate Review Needed.

Unit 2: Writing — Chapter 1: Prewriting (cont.)

Review Skill / Mastered Skill

	Lessons 1	2	3	4	5	6	7	8	9	Un.Rev	End Rev
Standard 3.2 (Writing) All students will write in clear, concise, organized language that varies in content and form for different audiences and purposes.											
A11. WRITING AS A PROCESS (PREWRITING, DRAFTING, REVISING, EDITING, POSTWRITING) Use computer word-processing applications during parts of the writing process.	○	○	○	○	○	★	★	✓	✓	✓	✓
B2. WRITING AS A PRODUCT (RESULTING IN A FORMAL PRODUCT OR PUBLICATION) Write a narrative piece based on personal experiences.	✓	✓	★	✓	✓	✓	✓	✓	✓	★	★
B3. WRITING AS A PRODUCT (RESULTING IN A FORMAL PRODUCT OR PUBLICATION) Write a nonfiction piece and/or simple informational report across the curriculum.	★	✓	✓	✓	✓	✓	✓	✓	✓	✓	★
B6. WRITING AS A PRODUCT (RESULTING IN A FORMAL PRODUCT OR PUBLICATION) Develop a collection of writings (e.g., a literacy folder or portfolio).	★	★	★	★	★	★	★	★	★	★	★
D1. WRITING FORMS, AUDIENCES, AND PURPOSES (EXPLORING A VARIETY OF FORMS) Write for a variety of purposes (e.g., to inform, entertain, persuade) and audiences (e.g., self, peers, community).	★	★	★	✓	✓	✓	✓	★	✓	★	★
D2. WRITING FORMS, AUDIENCES, AND PURPOSES (EXPLORING A VARIETY OF FORMS) Develop fluency by writing daily and for sustained amounts of time.	★	★	★	✓	✓	✓	✓	★	✓	★	★
D3. WRITING FORMS, AUDIENCES, AND PURPOSES (EXPLORING A VARIETY OF FORMS) Generate ideas for writing in a variety of situations and across the curriculum.	★	★	★	✓	★	✓	✓	★	✓	★	★
D4. WRITING FORMS, AUDIENCES, AND PURPOSES (EXPLORING A VARIETY OF FORMS) Write to express thoughts and ideas, to share experiences, and to communicate socially.	★	★	★	✓	★	✓	✓	★	✓	★	★
D5. WRITING FORMS, AUDIENCES, AND PURPOSES (EXPLORING A VARIETY OF FORMS) Write the events of a story sequentially.	○	★	✓	✓	✓	✓	✓	✓	★	★	★
D6. WRITING FORMS, AUDIENCES, AND PURPOSES (EXPLORING A VARIETY OF FORMS) Produce writing that demonstrates the use of a variety of sentence types, such as declarative, interrogative, exclamatory, and imperative.	○	○	○	○	★	✓	✓	✓	✓	★	★
D8. WRITING FORMS, AUDIENCES, AND PURPOSES (EXPLORING A VARIETY OF FORMS) Write narrative text (e.g., realistic, humorous, etc.).	○	★	✓	✓	✓	✓	✓	✓	✓	✓	★
D9. WRITING FORMS, AUDIENCES, AND PURPOSES (EXPLORING A VARIETY OF FORMS) Write non-fiction text (e.g., reports, procedures, and letters).	★	✓	★	✓	★	✓	✓	✓	✓	★	★

Unit 2: Writing — Chapter 2: Drafting

Review Skill / Mastered Skill

	Lessons 1	2	3	NA	NA	NA	NA	NA	NA	Un.Rev	End Rev
Standard 3.2 (Writing) All students will write in clear, concise, organized language that varies in content and form for different audiences and purposes.											
A1. WRITING AS A PROCESS (PREWRITING, DRAFTING, REVISING, EDITING, POSTWRITING) Generate possible ideas for writing through recalling experiences, listening to stories, reading, brainstorming, and discussion.	✓	✓	★							★	★
A3. WRITING AS A PROCESS (PREWRITING, DRAFTING, REVISING, EDITING, POSTWRITING) Use graphic organizers to assist with planning writing.	★	★	★							★	★
A4. WRITING AS A PROCESS (PREWRITING, DRAFTING, REVISING, EDITING, POSTWRITING) Compose first drafts from prewriting work.	✓	✓	★							★	★
A5. WRITING AS A PROCESS (PREWRITING, DRAFTING, REVISING, EDITING, POSTWRITING) Revise a draft by rereading for meaning, narrowing the focus, sequencing, elaborating with detail, improving openings, closings, and word choice to show voice.	○	○	★							★	★
A7. WRITING AS A PROCESS (PREWRITING, DRAFTING, REVISING, EDITING, POSTWRITING) Build awareness of ways authors use paragraphs to support meaning.	○	★	✓							★	✓

★ Standards covered   ○ Standards to be covered   ✓ Standards previously covered

Correlation to the New Jersey Core Curriculum Content Standards

This worktext is customized to the New Jersey Core Curriculum Content Standards and Cumulative Progress Indicators and will help you prepare for the New Jersey Grade Three Assessment of Skills and Knowledge (NJ ASK).

As the lesson for each Cumulative Progress Indicator (CPI) is completed, place a ✓ to indicate Mastery or an X to indicate Review Needed.

Unit 2: Writing Chapter 2: Drafting (cont.)	1	2	3	NA	NA	NA	NA	NA	NA	Un. Rev	End Rev
Standard 3.2 (Writing) All students will write in clear, concise, organized language that varies in content and form for different audiences and purposes.											
B1. WRITING AS A PRODUCT (RESULTING IN A FORMAL PRODUCT OR PUBLICATION) Write a descriptive piece, such as a description of a person, place, or object.	★	★	★							✓	★
B2. WRITING AS A PRODUCT (RESULTING IN A FORMAL PRODUCT OR PUBLICATION) Write a narrative piece based on personal experiences.	★	★	★							★	★
B3. WRITING AS A PRODUCT (RESULTING IN A FORMAL PRODUCT OR PUBLICATION) Write a nonfiction piece and/or simple informational report across the curriculum.	★	★	★							✓	★
B6. WRITING AS A PRODUCT (RESULTING IN A FORMAL PRODUCT OR PUBLICATION) Develop a collection of writings (e.g., a literacy folder or portfolio).	★	★	★							★	★
D1. WRITING FORMS, AUDIENCES, AND PURPOSES (EXPLORING A VARIETY OF FORMS) Write for a variety of purposes (e.g., to inform, entertain, persuade) and audiences (e.g., self, peers, community).	★	★	★							★	★
D2. WRITING FORMS, AUDIENCES, AND PURPOSES (EXPLORING A VARIETY OF FORMS) Develop fluency by writing daily and for sustained amounts of time.	✓	✓	★							★	★
D3. WRITING FORMS, AUDIENCES, AND PURPOSES (EXPLORING A VARIETY OF FORMS) Generate ideas for writing in a variety of situations and across the curriculum.	✓	✓	★							★	★
D4. WRITING FORMS, AUDIENCES, AND PURPOSES (EXPLORING A VARIETY OF FORMS) Write to express thoughts and ideas, to share experiences, and to communicate socially.	★	★	★							★	★
D5. WRITING FORMS, AUDIENCES, AND PURPOSES (EXPLORING A VARIETY OF FORMS) Write the events of a story sequentially.	✓	★	★							★	★
D8. WRITING FORMS, AUDIENCES, AND PURPOSES (EXPLORING A VARIETY OF FORMS) Write narrative text (e.g., realistic, humorous, etc.).	✓	✓	★							★	★
D9. WRITING FORMS, AUDIENCES, AND PURPOSES (EXPLORING A VARIETY OF FORMS) Write non-fiction text (e.g., reports, procedures, and letters).	✓	✓	★							★	★

Unit 2: Writing Chapter 3: Revising	1	2	3	4	NA	NA	NA	NA	NA	Un. Rev	End Rev
Standard 3.2 (Writing) All students will write in clear, concise, organized language that varies in content and form for different audiences and purposes.											
A5. WRITING AS A PROCESS (PREWRITING, DRAFTING, REVISING, EDITING, POSTWRITING) Revise a draft by rereading for meaning, narrowing the focus, sequencing, elaborating with detail, improving openings, closings, and word choice to show voice.	★	✓	★	★						★	★
A6. WRITING AS A PROCESS (PREWRITING, DRAFTING, REVISING, EDITING, POSTWRITING) Participate with peers to comment on and react to each other's writing.	★	★	★	★						★	✓
A7. WRITING AS A PROCESS (PREWRITING, DRAFTING, REVISING, EDITING, POSTWRITING) Build awareness of ways authors use paragraphs to support meaning.	✓	✓	✓	★						★	✓
A8. WRITING AS A PROCESS (PREWRITING, DRAFTING, REVISING, EDITING, POSTWRITING) Begin to develop author's voice in own writing.	★	✓	★	★						★	★
A9. WRITING AS A PROCESS (PREWRITING, DRAFTING, REVISING, EDITING, POSTWRITING) Use reference materials to revise work, such as a dictionary or internet/software resource.	★	★	★	★						✓	✓
A10. WRITING AS A PROCESS (PREWRITING, DRAFTING, REVISING, EDITING, POSTWRITING) Edit work for basic spelling and mechanics.	★	✓	✓	✓						★	★

★ Standards covered   ○ Standards to be covered   ✓ Standards previously covered

Correlation to the New Jersey Core Curriculum Content Standards

This worktext is customized to the New Jersey Core Curriculum Content Standards and Cumulative Progress Indicators and will help you prepare for the New Jersey Grade Three Assessment of Skills and Knowledge (NJ ASK).

As the lesson for each Cumulative Progress Indicator (CPI) is completed, place a ✓ to indicate Mastery or an X to indicate Review Needed.

Unit 2: Writing
Chapter 3: Revising (cont.)

		Review Skill										
		Mastered Skill										
	Lessons	1	2	3	4	NA	NA	NA	NA	NA	Un.Rev	End Rev
Standard 3.2 (Writing) All students will write in clear, concise, organized language that varies in content and form for different audiences and purposes.												
A11. **WRITING AS A PROCESS** (PREWRITING, DRAFTING, REVISING, EDITING, POSTWRITING) Use computer word-processing applications during parts of the writing process.		★	★	★	★						✓	✓
A12. **WRITING AS A PROCESS** (PREWRITING, DRAFTING, REVISING, EDITING, POSTWRITING) Understand and use a checklist and/or rubric to improve writing.		★	★	★	★						★	★
A13. **WRITING AS A PROCESS** (PREWRITING, DRAFTING, REVISING, EDITING, POSTWRITING) Reflect on own writing, noting strengths and areas needing improvement.		★	★	★	★						★	✓
C1. **MECHANICS, SPELLING, HANDWRITING** Use Standard English conventions that are developmentally appropriate to the grade level: sentences, punctuation, capitalization, and spelling.		✓	★	✓	✓						★	★
C3. **MECHANICS, SPELLING, HANDWRITING** Study examples of narrative and expository writing to develop understanding of paragraphs and indentation.		✓	✓	✓	★						✓	✓
D6. **WRITING FORMS, AUDIENCES, AND PURPOSES** (EXPLORING A VARIETY OF FORMS) Produce writing that demonstrates the use of a variety of sentence types, such as declarative, interrogative, exclamatory, and imperative.		✓	★	✓	✓						★	★

Unit 2: Writing
Chapter 4: Editing

		Review Skill										
		Mastered Skill										
	Lessons	1	2	3	4	5	6	NA	NA	NA	Un.Rev	End Rev
Standard 3.2 (Writing) All students will write in clear, concise, organized language that varies in content and form for different audiences and purposes.												
A5. **WRITING AS A PROCESS** (PREWRITING, DRAFTING, REVISING, EDITING, POSTWRITING) Revise a draft by rereading for meaning, narrowing the focus, sequencing, elaborating with detail, improving openings, closings, and word choice to show voice.		★	★	★	★	★	★				★	★
A9. **WRITING AS A PROCESS** (PREWRITING, DRAFTING, REVISING, EDITING, POSTWRITING) Use reference materials to revise work, such as a dictionary or internet/software resource.		★	★	★	★	★	★				✓	✓
A10. **WRITING AS A PROCESS** (PREWRITING, DRAFTING, REVISING, EDITING, POSTWRITING) Edit work for basic spelling and mechanics.		★	★	★	★	★	★				★	★
A11. **WRITING AS A PROCESS** (PREWRITING, DRAFTING, REVISING, EDITING, POSTWRITING) Use computer word-processing applications during parts of the writing process.		✓	★	★	★	★	★				✓	✓
A13. **WRITING AS A PROCESS** (PREWRITING, DRAFTING, REVISING, EDITING, POSTWRITING) Reflect on own writing, noting strengths and areas needing improvement.		★	★	★	★	★	★				★	✓
C1. **MECHANICS, SPELLING, HANDWRITING** Use Standard English conventions that are developmentally appropriate to the grade level: sentences, punctuation, capitalization, and spelling.		★	★	★	✓	✓	✓				★	★
C2. **MECHANICS, SPELLING, HANDWRITING** Use grade-appropriate knowledge of English grammar and usage to craft writing: singular and plural nouns, subject/verb agreement, appropriate parts of speech.		✓	✓	✓	★	★	★				★	★
C4. **MECHANICS, SPELLING, HANDWRITING** Develop knowledge of English spelling through the use of patterns, structural analysis, and high frequency words.		★	✓	✓	✓	✓	✓				✓	★

★ Standards covered   O Standards to be covered   ✓ Standards previously covered

Correlation to the New Jersey Core Curriculum Content Standards

This worktext is customized to the New Jersey Core Curriculum Content Standards and Cumulative Progress Indicators and will help you prepare for the New Jersey Grade Three Assessment of Skills and Knowledge (NJ ASK).

As the lesson for each Cumulative Progress Indicator (CPI) is completed, place a ✓ to indicate Mastery or an X to indicate Review Needed.

Unit 2: Writing — Chapter 5: Postwriting

	1	2	NA	NA	NA	NA	NA	NA	NA	Un. Rev	End Rev
Standard 3.2 (Writing) All students will write in clear, concise, organized language that varies in content and form for different audiences and purposes.											
A4. WRITING AS A PROCESS (PREWRITING, DRAFTING, REVISING, EDITING, POSTWRITING) — Compose first drafts from prewriting work.	★	✓								★	★
A6. WRITING AS A PROCESS (PREWRITING, DRAFTING, REVISING, EDITING, POSTWRITING) — Participate with peers to comment on and react to each other's writing.	✓	★								★	✓
A11. WRITING AS A PROCESS (PREWRITING, DRAFTING, REVISING, EDITING, POSTWRITING) — Use computer word-processing applications during parts of the writing process.	★	✓								✓	✓
A12. WRITING AS A PROCESS (PREWRITING, DRAFTING, REVISING, EDITING, POSTWRITING) — Understand and use a checklist and/or rubric to improve writing.	★	★								★	★
A13. WRITING AS A PROCESS (PREWRITING, DRAFTING, REVISING, EDITING, POSTWRITING) — Reflect on own writing, noting strengths and areas needing improvement.	★	★								★	✓
B4. WRITING AS A PRODUCT (RESULTING IN A FORMAL PRODUCT OR PUBLICATION) — Present and discuss writing with other students.	★	✓								✓	✓
B5. WRITING AS A PRODUCT (RESULTING IN A FORMAL PRODUCT OR PUBLICATION) — Apply elements of grade-appropriate rubrics to improve writing.	O	★								★	✓
B6. WRITING AS A PRODUCT (RESULTING IN A FORMAL PRODUCT OR PUBLICATION) — Develop a collection of writings (e.g., a literacy folder or portfolio).	★	★								★	★
C5. MECHANICS, SPELLING, HANDWRITING — Write legibly in manuscript or cursive to meet district standards.	★	✓								★	★

Unit 3: Speaking and Listening

	1	2	3	4	5	NA	NA	NA	NA	NA	End Rev
Standard 3.1 (Reading) All students will understand and apply the knowledge of sounds, letters, and words in written English to become independent and fluent readers, and will read a variety of materials and texts with fluency and comprehension.											
C2. DECODING AND WORD RECOGNITION — Use letter-sound knowledge and structural analysis to decode words.	✓	✓	★	✓	✓						★
C3. DECODING AND WORD RECOGNITION — Use context to accurately read words with more than one pronunciation.	✓	✓	★	✓	✓						★
D1. FLUENCY — Recognize grade-level words accurately and with ease so that a text sounds like spoken language when read aloud.	★	★	✓	★	★						✓
D3. FLUENCY — Read aloud with proper phrasing, inflection, and intonation.	★	★	✓	★	★						✓
G11. COMPREHENSION SKILLS AND RESPONSE TO TEXT — Participate in creative responses to texts (e.g., dramatizations, oral presentations).	★	★	✓	★	★						✓
Standard 3.3 (Speaking) All students will speak in clear, concise, organized language that varies in content and form for different audiences and purposes.											
A1. DISCUSSION (SMALL GROUP AND WHOLE CLASS) — Listen and follow a discussion in order to contribute appropriately.	✓	✓	✓	✓	✓						✓
A2. DISCUSSION (SMALL GROUP AND WHOLE CLASS) — Stay focused on topic.	✓	✓	✓	✓	✓						✓

★ Standards covered   O Standards to be covered   ✓ Standards previously covered

Correlation to the New Jersey Core Curriculum Content Standards

This worktext is customized to the New Jersey Core Curriculum Content Standards and Cumulative Progress Indicators and will help you prepare for the New Jersey Grade Three Assessment of Skills and Knowledge (NJ ASK).

As the lesson for each Cumulative Progress Indicator (CPI) is completed, place a ✓ to indicate Mastery or an X to indicate Review Needed.

Unit 3: Speaking and Listening (cont.) — Review Skill / Mastered Skill / Lessons	1	2	3	4	5	NA	NA	NA	NA	Un.Rev	End Rev
Standard 3.3 (Speaking) All students will speak in clear, concise, organized language that varies in content and form for different audiences and purposes.											
A3. DISCUSSION (SMALL GROUP AND WHOLE CLASS) Take turns.	★	✓	✓	✓	✓						✓
A4. DISCUSSION (SMALL GROUP AND WHOLE CLASS) Support an opinion with details.	★	✓	✓	✓	✓						✓
B1. QUESTIONING (INQUIRY) AND CONTRIBUTING Develop appropriate questions to explore a topic.	✓	★	✓	✓	✓						✓
B2. QUESTIONING (INQUIRY) AND CONTRIBUTING Contribute information, ideas, and experiences to classroom inquiry.	✓	★	✓	✓	✓						✓
C1. WORD CHOICE Use vocabulary related to a particular topic.	✓	✓	★	✓	✓						✓
C2. WORD CHOICE Adapt language to persuade, explain, or seek information.	✓	✓	★	✓	✓						✓
C3. WORD CHOICE Use new vocabulary and figurative language learned from literature and classroom experiences.	✓	✓	★	✓	✓						✓
D1. ORAL PRESENTATION Use pictures to support an oral presentation.	✓	✓	✓	★	✓						✓
D2. ORAL PRESENTATION Attempt to revise future presentations based on feedback from peers and teacher.	✓	✓	✓	✓	★						✓
D3. ORAL PRESENTATION Use appropriate strategies to prepare, rehearse and deliver an oral presentation: word choice, expression, eye contact and volume.	✓	✓	✓	★	✓						✓
Standard 3.4 (Listening) All students will listen actively to information from a variety of sources in a variety of situations.											
A1. ACTIVE LISTENING Connect messages heard to prior knowledge and experiences.	✓	★	★	✓	✓						✓
A2. ACTIVE LISTENING Exchange information through verbal and nonverbal messages.	★	★	★	✓	✓						✓
B1. LISTENING COMPREHENSION Follow two- and three- step directions.	★	✓	✓	★	✓						✓
B2. LISTENING COMPREHENSION Listen to a story read aloud and/or information from television or film, and summarize main ideas.	★	✓	✓	★	✓						✓
B3. LISTENING COMPREHENSION Paraphrase information shared by others.	✓	✓	✓	★	✓						✓

★ Standards covered   O Standards to be covered   ✓ Standards previously covered

Holistic Writing

New Jersey Registered Holistic Scoring Rubric (Grades 3-4)

In Scoring, consider the grid of written language	Inadequate Command	Limited Command	Partial Command	Adequate Command	Strong Command
Score	**1**	**2**	**3**	**4**	**5**
Content & Organization	◆May lack opening and/or closing ◆Minimal response to topic; uncertain focus ◆No planning evident: disorganized ◆Details random, inappropriate, or barely apparent	◆May lack opening and/or closing ◆Attempts to focus ◆May drift or shift focus ◆Attempts organization ◆Few, if any, transitions between ideas ◆Details lack elaboration, i.e., highlight paper	◆May lack opening and/or closing ◆Usually has single focus ◆Some lapses or flaws in organization ◆May lack some transitions between ideas ◆Repetitious details ◆Several unelaborated details	◆Generally has opening and/or closing ◆Single focus ◆Ideas loosely connected ◆Transition evident ◆Uneven development of details	◆Opening and closing ◆Single focus ◆Sense of unity and coherence ◆Key ideas developed ◆Logical progression of ideas ◆Moderately fluent ◆Attempts compositional risks ◆Details appropriate and varied
Usage	◆No apparent control ◆Severe/numerous errors	◆Numerous errors	◆Errors/patterns of errors may be evident	◆Some errors that do not interfere with meaning	◆Few errors
Sentence Construction	◆Assortment of incomplete and/or incorrect sentences	◆Excessive monotony/same structure ◆Numerous errors	◆Little variety in syntax ◆Some errors	◆Some variety ◆Generally correct	◆Variety in syntax appropriate and effective ◆Few errors
Mechanics	◆Errors so severe they detract from meaning	◆Numerous serious errors	◆Patterns of errors evident	◆No consistent pattern of errors ◆Some errors that do not interfere with meaning	◆Few errors

Content & Organization	Usage	Sentence Construction	Mechanics
◆Communicates intended message to intended audience ◆Relates to topic ◆Opening and closing ◆Focused ◆Logical progression of ideas ◆Transitions ◆Appropriate details and information	◆Tense formation ◆Subject-verb agreement ◆Pronouns usage/agreement ◆Word choice/meaning ◆Proper modifiers	◆Variety of type, structure, and length ◆Correct construction	◆Spelling ◆Capitalization ◆Punctuation

NON-SCORABLE RESPONSES

OT (Off Topic/Off Task) Student did not write on the assigned topic/task, or the student attempted to copy the prompt.

NR (No Response) Student refused to write on the topic, or wrote too little to allow a reliable judgement of his/her writing.

OPEN-ENDED SCORING RUBRIC

For Reading, Listening, and Viewing

Sample Task: The author takes a strong position on voting rights for young people. Use information from the text to support your response to the following.

*Requirments:
- Explain the author's position on voting.
- Explain how adopting such a position would affect young people like you.

Points	Criteria
4	A 4-point response clearly demonstrates understanding of the task, completes all requirements, and provides an insightful explanation/opinion that links to or extends aspects of the text.
3	A 3-point response demonstrates an understanding of the task, completes all requirements, and provides some explanation/opinion using situations or ideas from the text as support.
2	A 2-point response may address all of the requirements, but demonstrates a partial understanding of the task, and uses text incorrectly or with limited success resulting in an inconsistent or flawed explanation.
1	A 1-point response demonstrates minimal understanding of the task, does not complete the requirements, and provides only a vague reference to or no use of the text.
0	A 0-point response is irrelevant or off-topic.

***Requirments for these items will vary according to the task.**

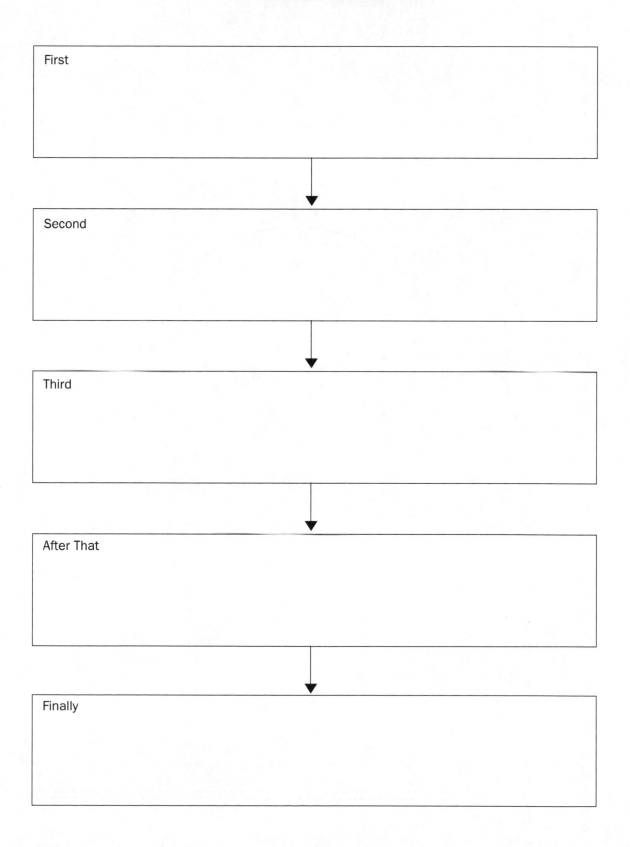

First

Second

Third

After That

Finally

KWL Chart

Topic _____

What I <u>K</u>now	What I <u>W</u>ant to Know	What I <u>L</u>earned

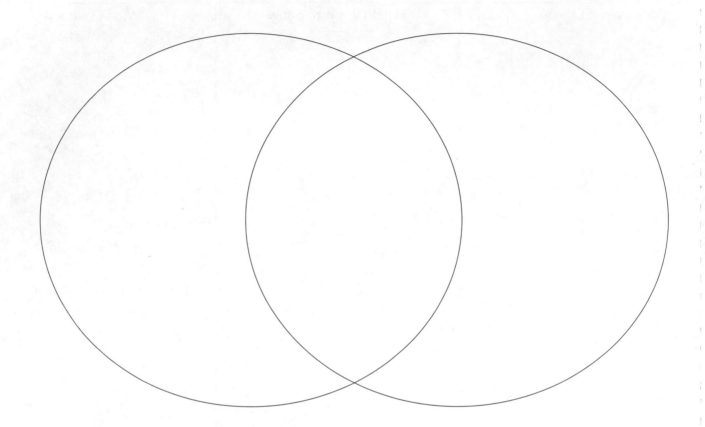

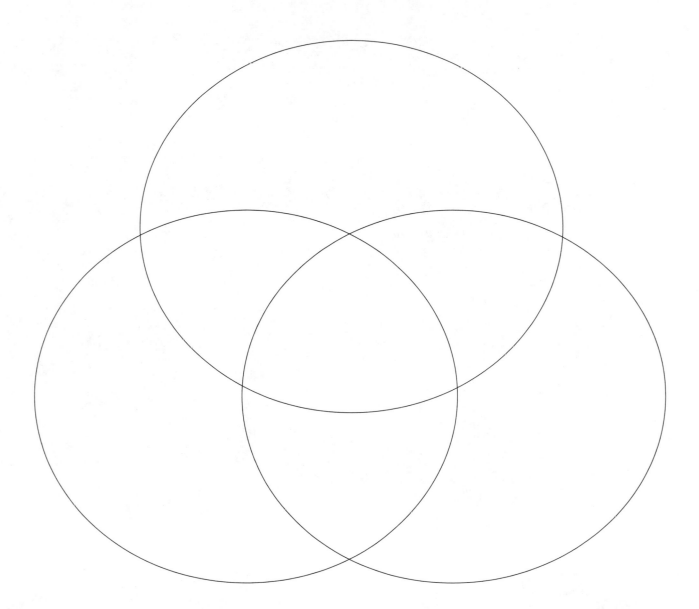

Notes